ABERDEEN UNIVERSITY STUDIES SERIES

Number 153

Energy Principles in Theory of Structures

Energy Principles in Theory of Structures

T. M. CHARLTON

Professor of Engineering in the University of Aberdeen
Foreign Member of the Finnish Academy of Technical Sciences

Published for the UNIVERSITY OF ABERDEEN
by
OXFORD UNIVERSITY PRESS
London New York Toronto
1973

Oxford University Press, Ely House, London W. 1
GLASGOW NEW YORK TORONTO MELBOURNE WELLINGTON
CAPE TOWN IBADAN NAIROBI DAR ES SALAAM LUSAKA ADDIS ABABA
DELHI BOMBAY CALCUTTA MADRAS KARACHI LAHORE DACCA
KUALA LUMPUR SINGAPORE HONG KONG TOKYO

ISBN 0 19 714102 1

Printed in Great Britain
at the University Press, Oxford
by Vivian Ridler
Printer to the University

Preface

THIS book is successor of the author's earlier work *Energy Principles in Applied Statics* (Blackie, 1959). One purpose of that book was to attempt to remove some of the confusion which was apparently widespread among engineers and students concerning the nature and use of the energy principles of engineering statics. Although there has been an enormous increase of sophistication in theory of structures during the intervening years, it seems doubtful whether there has been a commensurate understanding, in depth, of principles. That belief would of itself appear to justify the present work, though among its important and novel features are an elementary examination of the problem of approximate solutions including upper and lower bound aspect (Chapter VIII) and what is described as the *principle of virtual structures* (Appendix I). The latter affords a physical basis for virtual work procedures for calculating deflection of structures and has been found especially useful as a teaching device.

Confusion in respect of the energy principles of theory of structures was probably due originally to the description of Castigliano's well-known strain energy principle relating to strain compatibility within linearly elastic systems as the " principle of least work ". Having regard to the general mechanical principle of minimum potential energy relating to the stable equilibrium of conservative systems, that is an unfortunate misnomer as, it is hoped, is clearly demonstrated herein. Thus, the two basic approaches to the analysis of statically-indeterminate structures are necessarily considered explicitly and it is hoped that, in addition to clarifying energy principles, the reader will obtain an appreciation of the duality aspect. In passing, it is noteworthy that Castigliano's pupil Crotti included in his book of 1888 a remarkably general account of energy principles which was overlooked until quite recently.

In order to deal with the subject in the simplest general manner possible, attention is confined almost exclusively to plane pin-jointed systems. Moreover, the simple technical theory of bending of beams is based upon linearity, and the consideration of systems consisting of beams in bending with non-linear characteristics would introduce unjustifiable complications. It is not difficult, however, once the principles have been mastered, to apply them to statical systems of all kinds with the assistance of textbooks on theory of structures.

Perhaps the most valuable single energy principle is the oldest—the principle of virtual work. Fleeming Jenkin's early use of that principle (1869) in a striking manner followed his collaboration with Maxwell in theory of structures, which began (at Jenkin's instigation) seemingly in 1861. It is of immense value for calculating deflections of structures and is the basis of the complementary-energy principle.

The main practical value of the potential- and complementary-energy principles lies in their affording means of obtaining approximate solutions to complex problems relatively easily. Since this aspect constitutes a specialist subject in itself, only the basic idea is given herein with a worked example.

Finally, I wish to express my gratitude to the University of Aberdeen for undertaking publication of this work. Also to friends and colleagues, including Professor Sir John Baker, F.R.S., Professor Arvo Ylinen, Dr. J. A. L. Matheson, C.M.G., M.B.E., and Dr. M. S. Gregory, for generous encouragement over a number of years. Then to Mrs. Heather Flett for invaluable assistance in preparing the manuscript for publication.

T. M. CHARLTON

Aberdeen, 1973

Contents

I Introduction

1. The first contact which many engineers can remember having with minimum-energy principles occurred when as students they were taught a method of analysing linear elastic statically-indeterminate frames using Castigliano's principle of least work (1873). The ease with which this principle can be applied to demonstrate an approach to the analysis of such frames (without the necessity of protracted thought), together with the apparent manifestation of economy of nature which is frequently regarded as axiomatic, usually makes a profound impression. Moreover, it seems as though Castigliano's method is no more than a particular application of the principle of minimum potential energy for conservative systems * which is sometimes studied in an abstract fashion in courses in elementary mechanics, though illustration of its practical applications is often neglected.

This kind of confusion concerning two distinct energy principles was also evident in some early accounts of Castigliano's work which were published in this country.† The correct appreciation of Castigliano's principle was, however, greatly facilitated by the efforts of Engesser (1889). Engesser's work called attention to a quantity which he called " complementary energy " which can be used as a mathematical device to derive deflections of systems with either linear or non-linear elasticity. It is easy to show that Castigliano used the real work or strain energy of systems with linear elasticity (in accordance with Hooke's law) in the capacity of complementary energy. This interchangeability of strain and complementary energy is possible only for systems with certain special characteristics and, quite apart from its being unnecessary, it is really indefensible on purely mathematical grounds. Thus, while Castigliano's principle of least work is concerned with compatibility or " equilibrium " of deflections, the principle of minimum potential energy, involving the use of real energy quantities (such as strain energy) to derive forces, is concerned with equilibrium of forces. Moreover, this use of potential energy is not restricted to systems with linear characteristics.

* Systems for which mechanical energy is conserved.

† See, for example, H. M. Martin (1895).

Without anticipating the contents of later Chapters it is not possible to elaborate these introductory remarks further. They are made for the purpose of calling attention to the kind of pitfall which awaits the unwary in the pursuit of a subject which several generations of engineers with a taste for theoretical matters have found fascinating but elusive. The power of minimum-energy principles in practice lies in their adaptability for obtaining with relative ease sufficiently accurate approximate solutions to many problems which might otherwise be intractable by manual effort.

It is perhaps true to say that any mystery and confusion which surrounds minimum-energy principles is due in no small measure to a superficial approach to the concept of the economy of nature, a concept which was given considerable prominence by natural philosophers during the nineteenth century.

2. Strain energy and complementary energy.

In the above introductory remarks three energy quantities which are useful in the study of conservative systems are mentioned: namely potential energy, strain energy, and complementary energy. It is perhaps preferable to consider the last two quantities in some detail before dealing with potential energy, even though strain energy is frequently identifiable with potential energy. Suppose the elastic spring shown in fig. I.1 is subjected to a gradually increasing force F; then, if its load-deflection characteristic is non-linear, the force F might be related to the extension y of the spring in the manner described by the curve OB shown in fig. I.2. The area OBD below and to the right of the curve represents the work done upon the spring by the force, therefore, by the law of conservation of energy, the strain energy stored in the spring is given by

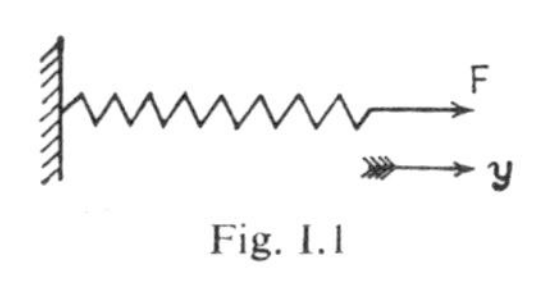

Fig. I.1

$$U = \int_0^y F\,dy \tag{I.1}$$

Clearly, differentiation of the strain energy gives

$$\frac{dU}{dy} = F \tag{I.2}$$

the force applied to the spring when the extension has any value y.

Consideration of the area ABO above and to the left of the curve shown in fig. I.2 shows that it represents

$$C = \int_0^F y\,dF \tag{I.3}$$

a quantity which Engesser has called the complementary energy. Differentiation of the complementary energy gives

$$\frac{dC}{dF} = y \tag{I.4}$$

the extension of the spring when the load has any value F. Complementary energy is a mathematical quantity and has, in general, no physical status. It is, however, interesting to compare it with the quantity $\int v\,dp$

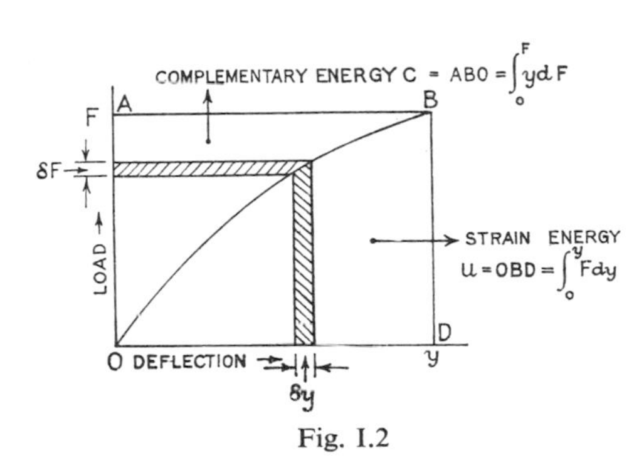

Fig. I.2

which arises in the study of the thermodynamics of perfect gases, v being the volume and p the pressure. As such a comparison is largely of academic interest and not essential for the present purpose, it is not proposed to consider it in detail in this book.

3. Interchangeability of strain energy and complementary energy.

After defining strain energy and complementary energy it is instructive to consider the possibility of their interchangeability for the purpose of analytical processes. First of all, it should be noted that the result of differentiating either the strain-energy function or the complementary-energy function with respect to a deflection has the dimension of a force, while the result of differentiating either with respect to a force has the dimension of a length (or deflection). It is, however, clear from fig. I.2 that the results of these differentiations can, in general, only be identified readily with physical quantities when strain energy is used for the purpose of deriving force and complementary energy is used for the purpose of deriving deflection. Nevertheless, there are kinds of system for which, for mathematical purposes, the strain and complementary energies are interchangeable.

One kind of system in this category is that for which force and deflection are related in the manner $F = by^n$, where b is a constant coefficient and n is a constant exponent. The linear system (for example, a spring of which the deflection is directly proportional to the force applied to it) represents a particular system of this kind for which $n = 1$. Now the strain and complementary energies when n has any real value are respectively

$$U = \int_0^y F\,dy = b\int_0^y y^n\,dy = \frac{1}{nb^{1/n}}\int_0^F F^{1/n}\,dF$$

$$C = \int_0^F y\,dF = \frac{1}{b^{1/n}}\int_0^F F^{1/n}\,dF = bn\int_0^y y^n\,dy \qquad \text{(I.5)}$$

Therefore

$$\frac{dU}{dy} = F; \quad \frac{dU}{dF} = \frac{1}{n}\left(\frac{F}{b}\right)^{1/n} = \frac{1}{n}y \qquad \text{(I.6)}$$

$$\frac{dC}{dF} = y; \quad \frac{dC}{dy} = bny^n = nF \qquad \text{(I.7)}$$

When $n = 1$

$$\frac{dU}{dF} = y \qquad \text{(I.8)}$$

$$\frac{dC}{dy} = F \qquad \text{(I.9)}$$

Thus, when $n = 1$, the strain and complementary energies are completely interchangeable (fig. I.3) but when n has any other real value the factor

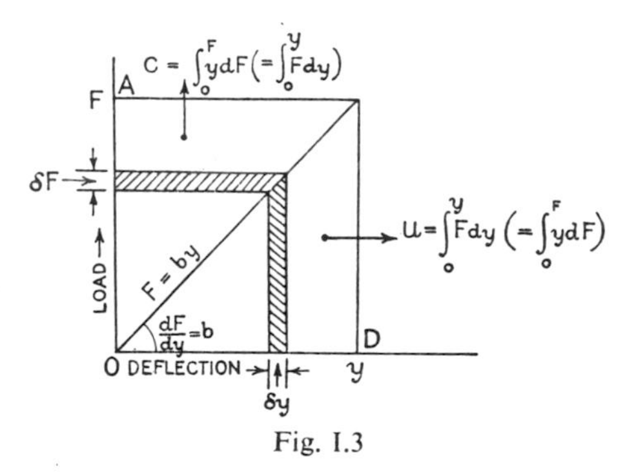

Fig. I.3

$1/n$ or n, as the case may be, is required if use is to be made of this mathematical property of interchangeability.

It is necessary to emphasize here that there is no advantage whatsoever in making use of the interchangeability of strain and complementary energies. In fact it can be classed as trivial and is contrary to appreciation of basic principles. Unfortunately it continues to appeal to those who are prejudiced concerning the mathematical use of a quantity (complementary energy) which lacks physical status.

Equation (I.8) is embodied in what is usually referred to as Castigliano's first theorem of strain energy, and his so-called principle of least work represents a form of his second theorem of strain energy, the derivation of which is based upon the first theorem. As an engineer, Castigliano was mainly concerned with materials of construction which had linear force-deflection characteristics, in accordance with Hooke's law, so it is not really surprising that, having discovered the possibility of using strain energy to obtain deflections of linear systems, he did not proceed to consider the general problem. Moreover, Castigliano's work was acclaimed by many of his contemporaries (including Müller-Breslau) and it became particularly fashionable in academic institutions. The unfortunate result has been the misunderstanding of the basic aspects of the various energy methods by many engineers ever since.

4. Potential energy.

The concept of potential energy, the energy which a system possesses by virtue of its configuration or position, is also conveniently illustrated by reference to a simple spring. Whereas it is unnecessary to specify the derivation of the force applied to the spring for the purpose of considering its strain energy and complementary energy, it is essential to do so for the purpose of considering potential energy. Thus, the assumption of a gravitational force is ideal because it is derived from the best-known source of potential energy, the mathematical expression of which is exceedingly simple.

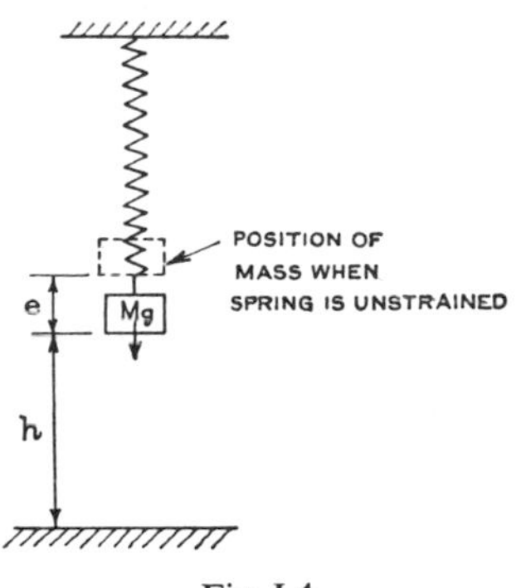

Fig. I.4

Suppose a mass M under the influence of gravity is suspended by a spring of negligible mass, and that the system (consisting of the spring and the mass) is at rest, as shown in fig. I.4. The potential energy of the system consists of two components: the strain energy of the spring, and the energy of the mass due to the effect of gravity. Denoting the potential energy by V, its mathematical expression is as follows:

$$V = U + Mgh + K \tag{I.10}$$

where $U = \int_0^e F\,dy$ is the strain energy of the spring, e is the total extension of the spring due to the suspension of the mass M, g is the acceleration due to gravity, h is the height of M with reference to an arbitrary datum, and K is the gravitational potential energy of M at the arbitrarily chosen datum. If, however, the potential energy is referred to a datum for gravitational potential energy which coincides with the lower part of the mass with the spring in the unstrained condition, then

$$V = U - Mge + K' \tag{I.11}$$

where $K' = K + Mg(h + e)$. It should be noted that while both h and e are variable their sum is constant. This latter is the useful form of the potential-energy function and it can be differentiated with respect to e as follows:

$$\frac{dV}{de} = \frac{dU}{de} - Mg \tag{I.12}$$

But dU/de represents the force on the mass when its extension is e so that in this instance $dU/de = Mg$, therefore it is clear that $dV/de = 0$. This result is in accordance with the principle of stationary potential energy for systems in equilibrium which is considered in more detail in Chapter II.

From equations (I.10) and (I.11) it appears (fig. I.5) that there is a loss of energy represented by $(U - Mge)$ when a mass under the influence of gravity is transferred to a spring. In order to explain this feature it is

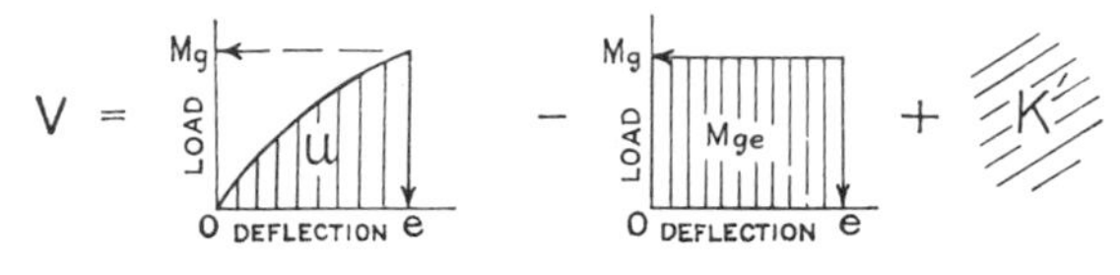

Fig. I.5

necessary to examine in detail the process whereby the mass is suspended. First of all an agency external to the mass-spring system, for example, a human being, must place the hook on the mass in contact with the hook on the spring. The load must then be gradually transferred from the external agency to the spring so that, when the transfer is complete and the external agency is removed, the system is at rest. At any instant during the transfer of load to the spring, part of the gravitational force on the mass is carried by the spring and the remainder is carried by the external agency. These portions of the total force Mg are shown graphically in fig. I.6 in relation to the extension of the spring, which is assumed for the sake of generality to vary in a non-linear manner with the load on the spring. The areas under these curves represent the work done by the gravitational force upon the spring and upon the external agency respectively. Their sum is Mge and the latter quantity represents the loss of energy from the mass-spring system $(U - Mge)$.*

5. Sudden application of load.

The alternative to the gradual transfer of a mass under the influence of gravity to a spring is the instantaneous release of the mass by the external agency as soon as it is in contact with the hook of the spring. This kind of transfer causes motion of the mass-spring system because, at the instant following release of the mass by the external agency, the gravitational force on the mass has no opposition from the spring since the latter is unstrained. The downward motion of the mass is eventually arrested by the force exerted by the spring since it increases as the extension increases, but then upward motion follows because, owing to the

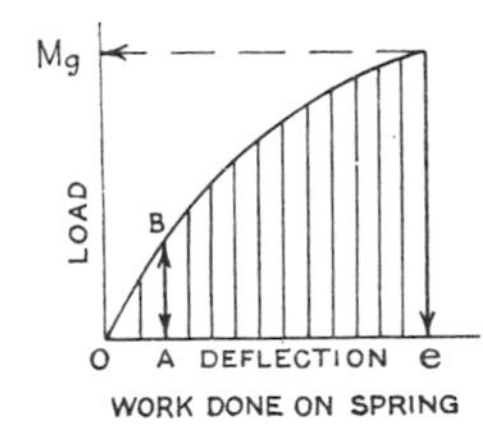

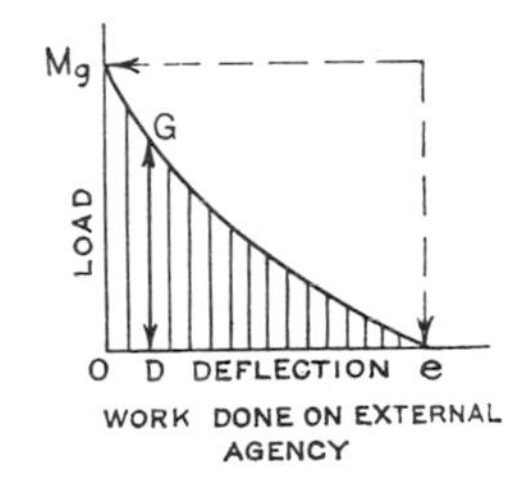

AB + DG = Mg

Fig. I.6

force necessary to destroy the motion of the mass, the upward force exerted by the spring exceeds Mg at the instant of no motion. In fact, oscillatory motion of the system takes place, the amplitude of which can be found by applying the law of conservation of energy in the following manner. If the distance through which the mass falls before it is arrested by the spring is s, the corresponding loss of potential energy of the mass is

$$V_0 - V_s = Mgs$$

By the law of conservation of energy, this loss of potential energy of the mass must be equal to the energy stored in the spring during the motion through the distance s because there is no external influence upon the

* The work done on the external agency in this instance is thus identifiable with the complementary energy of the spring. It is, however, most important to remember that their mathematical definitions are quite different; the former is $\int_0^e (Mg - F)\, dy$ while the latter is $\int_0^{Mg} y dF$.

system other than gravity. The strain energy stored in the spring is

$$U = \int_0^s F\,dy$$

Therefore

$$Mgs = \int_0^s F\,dy$$

or

$$s = \frac{1}{Mg}\int_0^s F\,dy \tag{I.13}$$

If the spring has a linear load-deflection characteristic, its restoring force $F = by$ and equation (I.13) can be rewritten

$$s = \frac{b}{Mg}\int_0^s y\,dy = \frac{bs^2}{2Mg}$$

or

$$s = \frac{2Mg}{b} \tag{I.14}$$

Under conditions of the weight due to the mass being transferred to the spring gradually as discussed in § 4 the final extension of the spring would be $e = Mg/b$, that is one-half of the amount during the motion following instantaneous application of the weight.

During the oscillatory motion of the system there will be a continuous interchange of energy between the spring and the mass in the absence of damping. Initially, potential energy of the mass is transferred to the spring, and then the process is reversed, and so on. It is appropriate to remark here that in general free oscillatory motion is the result of a small displacement of a conservative system from its configuration of stable equilibrium. It will be recalled that the elementary definition of a position of stable equilibrium is that position of equilibrium to which a system tends to return following a small displacement. Oscillatory motion is thus the manifestation of the tendency to regain a position of stable equilibrium. This aspect is considered in more detail in Chapter II, § 15.

6. Conservation of energy.

Reference has been made several times already to the law of conservation of energy, which is believed to be a basic law of nature. This law is essential for all energy methods. An objection to the use in analysis of the mathematical quantity " complementary energy " can be made on the grounds that it is not subject to the law of conservation of energy, because it cannot generally be identified with a physical quantity. Fortunately, however, it is possible to show that complementary energy is conserved in certain circumstances which are usually present in statical systems such as engineering structures. The principle of virtual work is the means whereby conservation of complementary energy can be demonstrated. The principle of virtual work is concerned with the application of the law of conservation of energy when geometrically possible small displacements of a system in stable equilibrium are imagined to occur. The principle is, in fact, an ingenious application of the law of conservation of energy, although it can be derived from the condition that the potential energy of a system in stable equilibrium is a minimum. Both aspects of the principle are considered at some length in Chapter IV.

7. Conclusion.

In this Chapter the idea of energy methods is introduced by reference to a system with one degree of freedom; generalizations are left over to subsequent Chapters in order that basic concepts shall not be obscured by too much detail. The use of energy quantities, such as potential energy and kinetic energy, for the derivation of equations of motion in the study of the dynamics of conservative systems is possible, but this aspect is outside the scope of this book. Westergaard* has proposed the use of complementary energy in dynamics, but his work does not really show any advantage of its use for such a purpose.

* See reference 14 of the Bibliography.

II Conditions of Equilibrium by Energy Methods: The Methods of Strain Energy and Potential Energy

1. Introduction.

By virtue of their properties which are considered briefly in Chapter I, strain energy and, in a more general sense, potential energy can be used for setting up equations of equilibrium of conservative statical systems. In addition, the latter provides a criterion of stability. This Chapter is concerned with these aspects. The method of strain energy, when it is appropriate, is merely a direct application of the law of conservation of energy, so that a formal proof is hardly necessary. The precise details of this method, which is considered first in this Chapter, are best explained by means of simple examples.

2. The strain-energy method.

The strain-energy method for elastic systems will be demonstrated initially for deriving the equations of equilibrium for the simple pin-jointed elastic structure with two degrees of freedom, loaded as shown in fig. II.1. It will be assumed in the first instance that the load does not cause gross distortion; that is, that the geometry of the structure after loading is essentially the same as that in the unloaded condition. This assumption is usually valid for engineering structures and it signifies that the changes in length of the members due to loading are small in comparison with any dimension of the structure.

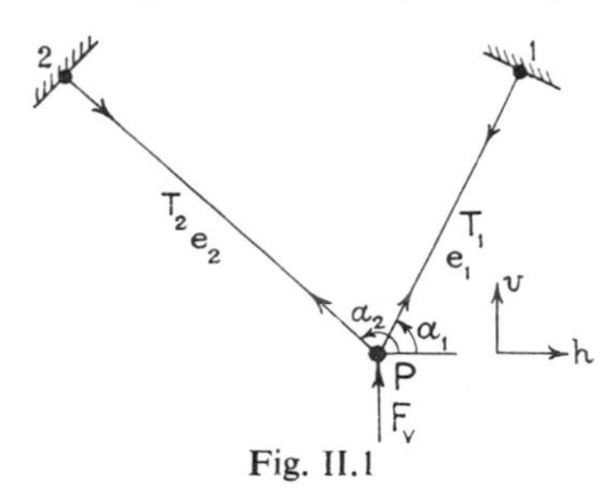

Fig. II.1

Assuming tensile forces T_1 and T_2 respectively in the bars or members of the structure due to the load F_V and that the corresponding increases in length of the members are e_1 and e_2 respectively, which are compatible with the independent vertical and horizontal deflections v and h (fig. II.1) of the joint P, a small increase δF_V in the load will cause changes δT_1,

δT_2, δe_1, δe_2, δv and δh in these quantities. The increase in the strain energy of the structure δU due to the additional work done by the load δW is, by the law of conservation of energy,

$$\delta W = F_V \delta v = \delta U = T_1\,\delta e_1 + T_2\,\delta e_2 \tag{II.1}$$

when small quantities of the second order of magnitude are neglected. Therefore

$$\begin{aligned} \frac{\partial U}{\partial v} &= T_1 \frac{\partial e_1}{\partial v} + T_2 \frac{\partial e_2}{\partial v} = \frac{\partial W}{\partial v} = F_V \\ \frac{\partial U}{\partial h} &= T_1 \frac{\partial e_1}{\partial h} + T_2 \frac{\partial e_2}{\partial h} = \frac{\partial W}{\partial h} = 0 \end{aligned} \tag{II.2}$$

which are equations of equilibrium of P. Before further progress can be made, account must be taken of the geometrical relationships between δv, δh, δe_1 and δe_2. With increases in length of the members as positive, the following relationships are obtained by observing that δe_1 and δe_2 are equal to the resolved components of δv and δh in the lines of the members, which are at angles α_1 and α_2 to the direction of h respectively:

$$\begin{aligned} \delta e_1 &= -\delta v \sin \alpha_1 - \delta h \cos \alpha_1 \\ \delta e_2 &= -\delta v \sin \alpha_2 - \delta h \cos \alpha_2 \end{aligned} \tag{II.3}$$

whence

$$\begin{aligned} \frac{\partial e_1}{\partial v} &= -\sin \alpha_1 \qquad & \frac{\partial e_1}{\partial h} &= -\cos \alpha_1 \\ \frac{\partial e_2}{\partial v} &= -\sin \alpha_2 \qquad & \frac{\partial e_2}{\partial h} &= -\cos \alpha_2 \end{aligned} \tag{II.4}$$

Substituting these expressions in equations (II.2) gives

$$\begin{aligned} \frac{\partial U}{\partial v} &= -T_1 \sin \alpha_1 - T_2 \sin \alpha_2 = \frac{\partial W}{\partial v} = F_V \\ \frac{\partial U}{\partial h} &= -T_1 \cos \alpha_1 - T_2 \cos \alpha_2 = \frac{\partial W}{\partial h} = 0 \end{aligned} \tag{II.5}$$

Equations (II.5) are the form of the conditions of equilibrium of the joint P when forces are resolved vertically and horizontally, assuming that T_1 and T_2 are tensile. (Had the members been inextensible the same equations could have been obtained in a similar way by using the principle of virtual or imaginary work as in Chapter IV, § 3.)

When the forces in the members T_1 and T_2 have been found by solving equations (II.5) it is a simple matter to find the deflections v and h of P by using geometrical relationships similar to those of equations (II.3) together with the law of elasticity* relating T_1 and e_1 and T_2 and e_2.

3. The effect of gross distortion.

In the event of the occurrence of gross distortion of the structure due, say, to very high flexibility of the members, the angles α_1 and α_2 might become α_1' and α_2' when the structure is loaded, as shown in fig. II.2. Because, however, energy variation is made with reference to the loaded

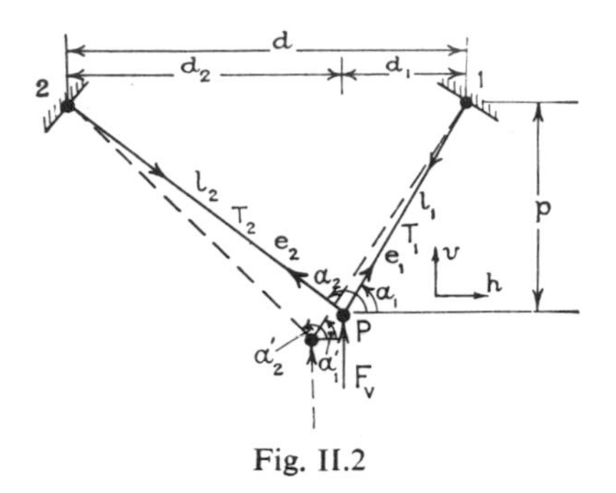

Fig. II.2

condition of the structure, the form of equations (II.1) to (II.5) inclusive is unchanged, but α_1' and α_2', which specify the inclination of the members in the loaded configuration, must be substituted for α_1 and α_2 respectively. Thus the equilibrium equations (II.5) become

$$\begin{aligned} -T_1 \sin\alpha_1' - T_2 \sin\alpha_2' &= F_V \\ -T_1 \cos\alpha_1' - T_2 \cos\alpha_2' &= 0 \end{aligned} \qquad \text{(II.6)}$$

where α_1' and α_2' are unknowns as well as T_1 and T_2. Two additional equations are therefore necessary to enable the problem to be solved and can be obtained from geometrical considerations as follows:

$$\begin{aligned} (l_1+e_1)\sin\alpha_1' &= (l_2+e_2)\sin\alpha_2' \\ (l_1+e_1)\cos\alpha_1' - (l_2+e_2)\cos\alpha_2' &= d \end{aligned} \qquad \text{(II.7)}$$

where l_1 and l_2 are the original lengths of the members respectively, d is the distance between joints 1 and 2, and e_1 and e_2 can be expressed in

* Thus if the elasticity of the members is linear, such that $e_1 = a_1 T_1$ and $e_2 = a_2 T_2$, then

$$e_1 = a_1 T_1 = -v \sin\alpha_1 - h\cos\alpha_1$$
$$e_2 = a_2 T_2 = -v \sin\alpha_2 - h\cos\alpha_2$$

whereby v and h can be found when T_1 and T_2 are known since a_1 and a_2 are the constant flexibility coefficients of the members respectively.

terms of T_1 and T_2 respectively by means of the load-deflection characteristics of the members. Equations (II.6) and (II.7) are, therefore, sufficient for the purpose of solving the problem.

4. Alternative application of strain energy for dealing with gross distortion.

A more sophisticated approach to the problem of gross distortion is possible by the strain-energy method, however. If, for reasons of simplicity, it is assumed that the members of the structure have linear elasticity so that $T_1 = b_1 e_1$ and $T_2 = b_2 e_2$, where b_1 and b_2 are the constant (stiffness) coefficients of the members, respectively*, equations (II.2) can be rewritten as follows:

$$\begin{aligned} \frac{\partial U}{\partial v} &= b_1 e_1 \frac{\partial e_1}{\partial v} + b_2 e_2 \frac{\partial e_2}{\partial v} = F_V \\ \frac{\partial U}{\partial h} &= b_1 e_1 \frac{\partial e_1}{\partial h} + b_2 e_2 \frac{\partial e_2}{\partial h} = 0 \end{aligned} \qquad \text{(II.8)}$$

Applying Pythagoras' theorem to the loaded configuration of the structure, and assuming that e_1, e_2, v and h are positive (fig. II.2),

$$\begin{aligned} (l_1 + e_1)^2 &= (d_1 - h)^2 + (p - v)^2 \\ (l_2 + e_2)^2 &= (d_2 + h)^2 + (p - v)^2 \end{aligned} \qquad \text{(II.9)}$$

Therefore

$$\begin{aligned} e_1 &= \sqrt{[(d_1 - h)^2 + (p - v)^2]} - l_1 \\ e_2 &= \sqrt{[(d_2 + h)^2 + (p - v)^2]} - l_2 \end{aligned} \qquad \text{(II.10)}$$

and

$$\begin{aligned} \frac{\partial e_1}{\partial v} &= -\frac{(p - v)}{\sqrt{[(d_1 - h)^2 + (p - v)^2]}} \\ \frac{\partial e_1}{\partial h} &= -\frac{(d_1 - h)}{\sqrt{[(d_1 - h)^2 + (p - v)^2]}} \\ \frac{\partial e_2}{\partial v} &= -\frac{(p - v)}{\sqrt{[(d_2 + h)^2 + (p - v)^2]}} \\ \frac{\partial e_2}{\partial h} &= +\frac{(d_2 + h)}{\sqrt{[(d_2 + h)^2 + (p - v)^2]}} \end{aligned} \qquad \text{(II.11)}$$

* The stiffness coefficients b_1 and b_2 are the reciprocals of the flexibility coefficients a_1 and a_2 respectively.

Substituting in equations (II.8) from equations (II.10) and (II.11)

$$\frac{\partial U}{\partial v} = -b_1\left(\frac{\sqrt{[(d_1-h)^2+(p-v)^2]}-l_1}{\sqrt{[(d_1-h)^2+(p-v)^2]}}\right)(p-v)-$$
$$b_2\left(\frac{\sqrt{[(d_2+h)^2+(p-v)^2]}-l_2}{\sqrt{[(d_2+h)^2+(p-v)^2]}}\right)(p-v) = F_V$$

$$\frac{\partial U}{\partial h} = -b_1\left(\frac{\sqrt{[(d_1-h)^2+(p-v)^2]}-l_1}{\sqrt{[(d_1-h)^2+(p-v)^2]}}\right)(d_1-h)+$$
$$b_2\left(\frac{\sqrt{[(d_2+h)^2+(p-v)^2]}-l_2}{\sqrt{[(d_2+h)^2+(p-v)^2]}}\right)(d_2+h) = 0 \qquad \text{(II.12)}$$

Equations (II.12) are non-linear simultaneous equations in v and h, the components of the deflection of P, and are another form of the equations of equilibrium of P. It should be noted that although linear elasticity of the members is assumed, the elasticity of the structure as a whole is non-linear due to gross distortion. Having found v and h by equations (II.12), e_1 and e_2 can be found by equations (II.10) and hence the forces in the members because $T_1 = b_1e_1$ and $T_2 = b_2e_2$. Fortunately the majority of engineering structures are designed with a view to avoiding gross distortion, so that the analytical difficulties of solving non-linear simultaneous equations rarely arise in their analysis.

5. Strain-energy method for statically-indeterminate systems.

If the structure shown in fig. II.1 has additional members as shown in fig. II.3, since only two independent equations of equilibrium are available,

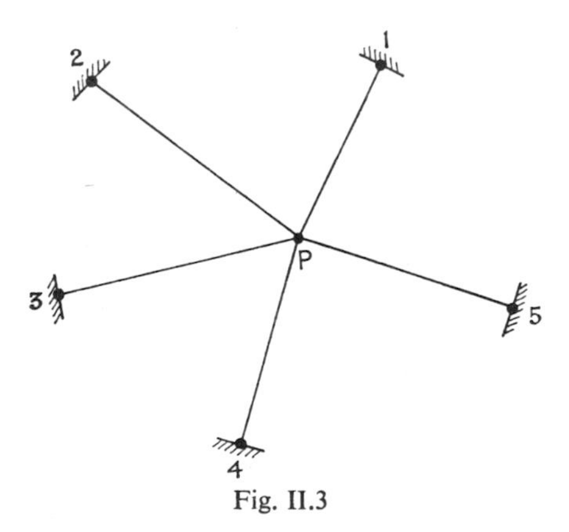

Fig. II.3

it is impossible to find the forces in the members merely by the principle of statics, even when gross distortion does not arise, and the system is said to be statically indeterminate. Sufficient additional information can, however, be obtained by considering the geometrical conditions which relate the changes in length of the members and the deflection components of the joint P.

For the purpose of illustrating the procedure using strain energy, suppose the structure has only one additional (redundant) member and is loaded by forces F_V and F_H as shown in fig. II.4. The conservation of energy equation due to a small change in one or both of the loads is

$$\delta U = T_1\,\delta e_1 + T_2\,\delta e_2 + T_3\,\delta e_3 = \delta W = F_V\,\delta v + F_H\,\delta h \qquad \text{(II.13)}$$

If, for the sake of simplicity, it is assumed that the members of the structure have linear elasticity so that $T_1 = b_1 e_1$, $T_2 = b_2 e_2$ and $T_3 = b_3 e_3$, equation (II.13) can be rewritten as follows:

$$\delta U = b_1 e_1\,\delta e_1 + b_2 e_2\,\delta e_2 + b_3 e_3\,\delta e_3 = F_V\,\delta v + F_H\,\delta h \qquad \text{(II.14)}$$

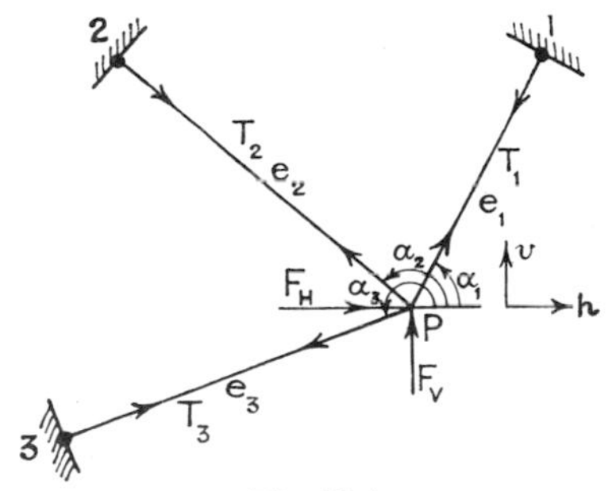

Fig. II.4

Thus

$$\frac{\partial U}{\partial v} = b_1 e_1 \frac{\partial e_1}{\partial v} + b_2 e_2 \frac{\partial e_2}{\partial v} + b_3 e_3 \frac{\partial e_3}{\partial v} = F_V$$

$$\frac{\partial U}{\partial h} = b_1 e_1 \frac{\partial e_1}{\partial h} + b_2 e_2 \frac{\partial e_2}{\partial h} + b_3 e_3 \frac{\partial e_3}{\partial h} = F_H \qquad \text{(II.15)}$$

The quantities e_1, e_2, e_3, v and h are not all independent, however, because they are subject to geometrical conditions of compatibility and if gross distortion does not occur these conditions can be obtained as in § 2, that is,

$$\begin{aligned} e_1 &= -v \sin\alpha_1 - h\cos\alpha_1 \\ e_2 &= -v \sin\alpha_2 - h\cos\alpha_2 \\ e_3 &= -v \sin\alpha_3 - h\cos\alpha_3 \end{aligned} \qquad \text{(II.16)}$$

and

$$\begin{aligned} \delta e_1 &= -\delta v \sin\alpha_1 - \delta h \cos\alpha_1 \\ \delta e_2 &= -\delta v \sin\alpha_2 - \delta h \cos\alpha_2 \\ \delta e_3 &= -\delta v \sin\alpha_3 - \delta h \cos\alpha_3 \end{aligned} \tag{II.17}$$

Substitution from equations (II.16) and (II.17)* in equations (II.15) gives

$$\begin{aligned} \frac{\partial U}{\partial v} &= b_1(v\sin\alpha_1 + h\cos\alpha_1)\sin\alpha_1 + b_2(v\sin\alpha_2 + h\cos\alpha_2)\sin\alpha_2 \\ &\qquad + b_3(v\sin\alpha_3 + h\cos\alpha_3)\sin\alpha_3 = F_V \\ \frac{\partial U}{\partial h} &= b_1(v\sin\alpha_1 + h\cos\alpha_1)\cos\alpha_1 + b_2(v\sin\alpha_2 + h\cos\alpha_2)\cos\alpha_2 \\ &\qquad + b_3(v\sin\alpha_3 + h\cos\alpha_3)\cos\alpha_3 = F_H \end{aligned} \tag{II.18}$$

or

$$\begin{aligned} \frac{\partial U}{\partial v} &= (b_1\sin^2\alpha_1 + b_2\sin^2\alpha_2 + b_3\sin^2\alpha_3)v \\ &\qquad + (b_1\sin\alpha_1\cos\alpha_1 + b_2\sin\alpha_2\cos\alpha_2 + b_3\sin\alpha_3\cos\alpha_3)h = F_V \\ \frac{\partial U}{\partial h} &= (b_1\sin\alpha_1\cos\alpha_1 + b_2\sin\alpha_2\cos\alpha_2 + b_3\sin\alpha_3\cos\alpha_3)v \\ &\qquad + (b_1\cos^2\alpha_1 + b_2\cos^2\alpha_2 + b_3\cos^2\alpha_3)h = F_H \end{aligned} \tag{II.19}$$

These equations are equations of equilibrium of the joint P with reference to the axes of v and h and are linear in terms of these deflection components. They can clearly be solved for the deflections v and h, and then the quantities e_1, e_2, and e_3 can be found by means of equations (II.16) and hence the forces in the members T_1, T_2 and T_3. Had gross distortion been involved, two non-linear simultaneous equations in v and h would have been obtained instead of the linear equations (II.19).

6. Reciprocal properties of coefficients of deflections (linear systems only).

It is interesting to note that equations (II.19) exhibit the reciprocal property (in accordance with the theorems of Maxwell, Betti, and Rayleigh) of systems with linear elasticity as a whole. The coefficients of

* It is instructive to substitute from equation (II.17) into equation (II.13), as follows:

$$\begin{aligned} \delta U = &-(\delta v \sin\alpha_1 + \delta h \cos\alpha_1)T_1 - (\delta v \sin\alpha_2 + \delta h \cos\alpha_2)T_2 \\ &-(\delta v \sin\alpha_3 + \delta h \cos\alpha_3)T_3 = \delta W = F_V\,\delta v + F_H\,\delta h \end{aligned}$$

whence

$$\frac{\partial U}{\partial v} = -T_1\sin\alpha_1 - T_2\sin\alpha_2 - T_3\sin\alpha_3 = F_V$$

$$\frac{\partial U}{\partial h} = -T_1\cos\alpha_1 - T_2\cos\alpha_2 - T_3\cos\alpha_3 = 0$$

which are the equations of equilibrium in terms of the forces in the members.

v and h in these equations are stiffness coefficients of the structure, that is, the equations can be rewritten in the form

$$\begin{aligned} b_{VV}v+b_{VH}h &= F_V \\ b_{HV}v+b_{HH}h &= F_H \end{aligned} \tag{II.20}$$

where $b_{VH} = b_{HV}$. The physical significance of stiffness coefficients of structures is considered in Chapter VII, § 10.

7. Number of final equations of equilibrium.

An interesting feature of the method of analysing a statically-indeterminate structure, whereby the equations of equilibrium are set up in terms of the components of the deflections of the joints as above, is that the number of the simultaneous equations (of equilibrium) to be solved finally is independent of the number of additional or redundant members. In fact, the number of equations is dictated by the number of independent components of deflection of joints or degrees of freedom which are involved. Thus for the example considered in § 5, since there are only two independent components of deflection, there are two final equations of equilibrium, no matter how many redundant members the system possesses. This is an important consideration in choosing the best method of approaching the analysis of a structure owing to the desirability of reducing the number of simultaneous equations to a minimum. (See also Chapter IV, § 10, Chapter V, § 7, and Chapter VII, § 14.)

8. The total potential-energy method.

Although strain energy enables the conditions of equilibrium for elastic systems to be formulated, the same object can be achieved for conservative systems generally by means of total potential energy as indicated in Chapter I, § 4. Moreover, the method of potential energy

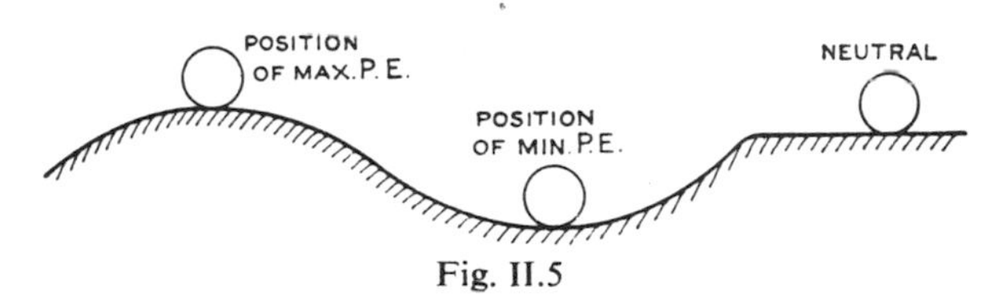

Fig. II.5

provides a criterion for the stability of conservative systems. It is shown in § 15 that the potential energy of a system in stable equilibrium is a minimum, while that of a system in unstable equilibrium is a maximum. A simple illustration of this feature of potential energy is shown in fig. II.5. The potential energy of the spherical body is due entirely to the gravitational field of force, and it is evident that, when it is a maximum, a small displacement of the sphere from this position of equilibrium will result in its departing from this position completely. If, however, the potential energy is a minimum, the sphere will tend to return to the position of equilibrium after a small displacement; in fact it will oscillate about the position of equilibrium. Again, if the sphere is in the neutral state, it is in equilibrium in all positions within a certain region and any small displacement is maintained.

9. Application of the potential-energy method.

Application of the method of potential energy can be illustrated by means of the example which was treated in § 5 (fig. II.4) by the strain-energy method. Since for equilibrium of a conservative system its potential energy V is stationary

$$\delta V = 0$$

The potential energy of an elastic system consists of the strain energy U of the system together with the potential energy of the loading. If, in writing an expression for δV, the small change δU in the strain energy is positive, then it follows that work has been done upon the structure by the loads so that the potential energy of the loading system has decreased correspondingly. Thus, for the example under consideration,

$$\delta V = \delta U - F_V\,\delta v - F_H\,\delta h = 0 \tag{II.21}$$

which is clearly in accordance with the law of conservation of energy (see equation II.13).

Therefore

$$\begin{aligned} \frac{\partial V}{\partial v} &= \frac{\partial U}{\partial v} - F_V = 0 \\ \frac{\partial V}{\partial h} &= \frac{\partial U}{\partial h} - F_H = 0 \end{aligned} \tag{II.22}$$

Now $\partial U/\partial v$ and $\partial U/\partial h$ are given by equations (II.19) and substitution in equations (II.22) gives

$$\begin{aligned} \frac{\partial V}{\partial v} &= (b_1 \sin^2\alpha_1 + b_2 \sin^2\alpha_2 + b_3 \sin^2\alpha_3)v + (b_1 \sin\alpha_1 \cos\alpha_1 \\ &\qquad + b_2 \sin\alpha_2 \cos\alpha_2 + b_3 \sin\alpha_3 \cos\alpha_3)h - F_V = 0 \\ \frac{\partial V}{\partial h} &= (b_1 \sin\alpha_1 \cos\alpha_1 + b_2 \sin\alpha_2 \cos\alpha_2 + b_3 \sin\alpha_3 \cos\alpha_3)v \\ &\qquad + (b_1 \cos^2\alpha_1 + b_2 \cos^2\alpha_2 + b_3 \cos^2\alpha_3)h - F_H = 0 \end{aligned} \tag{II.23}$$

These equations are essentially the same as equations (II.19), which is to be expected, because both the strain-energy and potential-energy methods for elastic systems are concerned with the derivation of conditions of equilibrium.

This single example is sufficient to illustrate the method of using potential energy in analysis. It is important to note, however, that for successful application of the potential- and strain-energy methods to elastic systems, the variation of strain energy must finally be expressed in terms of independent quantities representing deflections or deformations.

10. Criterion of stability by potential energy.

The question of whether the condition of equilibrium specified by equations (II.23) is stable or unstable depends upon whether these equations represent minimum or maximum potential energy. It is shown in textbooks on the calculus that a function V of two variables v and h is a minimum or a maximum if

$$\frac{\partial V}{\partial v} = \frac{\partial V}{\partial h} = 0$$

and

$$\frac{\partial^2 V}{\partial v^2} \cdot \frac{\partial^2 V}{\partial h^2} > \left(\frac{\partial^2 V}{\partial v \, . \, \partial h}\right)^2 \tag{II.24}$$

In addition, for a minimum $\partial^2 V/\partial v^2$ and $\partial^2 V/\partial h^2$ must be positive, and negative for a maximum. Without numerical values it is impossible to say whether all of these conditions are satisfied in a given instance. When, however, the elasticity of a system is linear as in the example of § 9, the part of the potential energy due to the strain energy is always positive, regardless of the sign of the variables, because it is entirely a function of the squares of the variables. The strain energy is, in fact, said to be a positive definite quadratic function and as such it has no maximum. Therefore, having regard to the form of the potential-energy function it may be concluded that equations (II.23) represent a minimum.

11. Non-linear systems.

There is nothing essentially novel in the application of either the method of strain energy or that of potential energy to the analysis of a statically-indeterminate non-linear elastic system. As the two methods are similar, the hypothetical pin-jointed structure with one redundant member and two degrees of freedom, shown in fig. II.6, is analysed below by the latter method. Member 1 has non-linear elasticity such that $T_1 =$

$b_1e_1^{1/2}$, and members 2 and 3 have linear elasticity such that $T_2 = b_2e_2$ and $T_3 = b_3e_3$ respectively. The anticipated deformations are as shown in fig. II.7: it is assumed that e_1, e_2 and e_3 are small in comparison with any dimension of the structure.

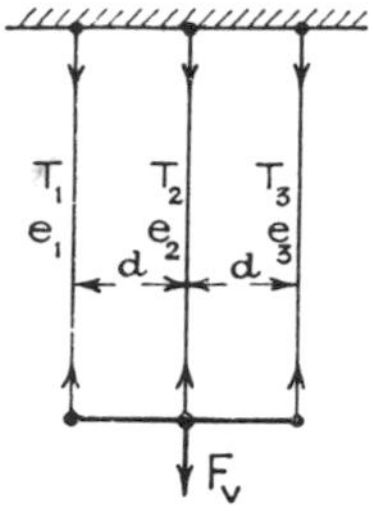

Fig. II.6

The condition for equilibrium using the total potential-energy method is

$$\delta V = \delta U - F_V \delta e_2 = 0$$

or

$$\delta V = T_1\,\delta e_1 + T_2\,\delta e_2 + T_3\,\delta e_3 - F_V\,\delta e_2 = 0 \qquad \text{(II.25)}$$

Now the condition for the geometrical compatibility of deformations is

$$\tfrac{1}{2}(e_1 + e_3) = e_2$$

or

$$e_1 = 2e_2 - e_3 \qquad \text{(II.26)}$$

and as there are two independent deflections, two independent equations of equilibrium are to be expected. Substituting, then, from equation (II.26) in (II.25) gives

$$\delta V = T_1(2\,\delta e_2 - \delta e_3) + T_2\,\delta e_2 + T_3\,\delta e_3 - F_V\,\delta e_2 = 0 \qquad \text{(II.27)}$$

so that

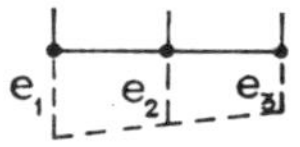

$$\left.\begin{aligned} \frac{\partial V}{\partial e_2} &= 2T_1 + T_2 - F_V = 0 \\ \frac{\partial V}{\partial e_3} &= -T_1 + T_3 = 0 \end{aligned}\right\} \qquad \text{(II.28)}$$

Fig. II.7

which are the required two independent equations of equilibrium of the system. The first is the condition for the equilibrium of forces, while the second is the condition for the equilibrium of moments. Substituting now for T_1, T_2, and T_3 their values in terms of the deformations e_1, e_2, and e_3 respectively, and remembering that $e_1 = 2e_2 - e_3$, gives the conditions of equilibrium in terms of deflections as follows:

$$\left.\begin{aligned} \frac{\partial V}{\partial e_2} &= 2b_1(2e_2 - e_3)^{\frac{1}{2}} + b_2e_2 - F_V = 0 \\ \frac{\partial V}{\partial e_3} &= -b_1(2e_2 - e_3)^{\frac{1}{2}} + b_3e_3 = 0 \end{aligned}\right\} \qquad \text{(II.29)}$$

These are non-linear simultaneous equations and are sufficient for the determination of e_2 and e_3, and hence e_1. They can, of course, be expressed alternatively in terms of T_2 and T_3, because $e_2 = T_2/b_2 = a_2T_2$, say, and $e_3 = T_3/b_3 = a_3T_3$; thus

$$\frac{2}{\sqrt{a_1}}(2a_2T_2 - a_3T_3)^{\frac{1}{2}} + T_2 - F_V = 0$$
$$-\frac{1}{\sqrt{a_1}}(2a_2T_2 - a_3T_3)^{\frac{1}{2}} + T_3 = 0 \qquad \text{(II.30)}$$

where $a_1 = 1/b_1^2$. Solution of equations (II.30) gives

$$T_2 = \frac{1}{2a_1}[2a_1F_V + 2(4a_2 + a_3) \pm 2\sqrt{\{(4a_2 + a_3)^2 + 8a_1a_2F_V\}}]$$

and (II.31)

$$T_3 = T_1 = -\frac{1}{2a_1}[(4a_2 + a_3) \pm \sqrt{\{(4a_2 + a_3)^2 + 8a_1a_2F_V\}}]$$

The form of equations (II.31) draws attention to an important aspect of the analysis of non-linear systems, namely, lack of uniqueness of the solution. In this solution a choice of signs is presented as in the solutions of similar problems involving non-linear elasticity. The appropriate signs have to be selected having regard to the physical aspects of the problem and by detailed examination of the alternatives. This aspect is also considered in Chapter III, § 5. In this instance the three members will clearly be in tension, so that the positive sign is appropriate in the expression for T_2 and the negative sign in the expression for T_1 and T_3.

12. Changing of variables or coordinates.

It is convenient at this point to introduce the idea of changing variables or coordinates. This idea can be demonstrated by reference to the example considered in § 11 above. Suppose it is desired to work throughout in terms of forces rather than deformations; the first step in general is to substitute for the deformations in terms of the relevant forces in the equations of compatibility. Thus the compatibility equation (II.26) becomes

$$a_1T_1{}^2 = 2a_2T_2 - a_3T_3 \qquad \text{(II.32)}$$

Therefore

$$T_1 = \sqrt{\left[\frac{1}{a_1}(2a_2T_2 - a_3T_3)\right]}$$

and since $\delta e_1 = 2\delta e_2 - \delta e_3$, also

$$\delta e_1 = 2a_2\,\delta T_2 - a_3\,\delta T_3 \qquad \text{(II.33)}$$

Substitution for T_1, δe_1, δe_2 and δe_3 in equation (II.25) gives

$$\delta V = \frac{1}{\sqrt{a_1}}(2a_2 T_2 - a_3 T_3)^{\frac{1}{2}}(2a_2 \delta T_2 - a_3 \delta T_3) + a_2 T_2 \delta T_2 + a_3 T_3 \delta T_3 - F_V a_2 \delta T_2 = 0$$

so that

$$\frac{\partial V}{\partial T_2} = 2\frac{a_2}{\sqrt{a_1}}(2a_2 T_2 - a_3 T_3)^{\frac{1}{2}} + a_2 T_2 - a_2 F_V = 0$$

$$\frac{\partial V}{\partial T_3} = -\frac{a_3}{\sqrt{a_1}}(2a_2 T_2 - a_3 T_3)^{\frac{1}{2}} + a_3 T_3 = 0 \qquad \text{(II.34)}$$

or

$$\frac{2}{\sqrt{a_1}}(2a_2 T_2 - a_3 T_3)^{\frac{1}{2}} + T_2 - F_V = 0$$

$$-\frac{1}{\sqrt{a_1}}(2a_2 T_2 - a_3 T_3)^{\frac{1}{2}} + T_3 = 0 \qquad \text{(II.35)}$$

which are identical to equations (II.30).

After taking note of the properties of strain and potential energy it is, perhaps, confusing to see equations of equilibrium derived by partial differentiation of potential energy with respect to force as in equation (II.34). It is emphasized, however, that in the above analysis the forces are merely representing the deformations; the conditions of geometrical compatibility were applied to deformations expressed in terms of the forces, in the variation of the potential energy. This procedure of changing coordinates (from deformations to forces representing them, in this instance) sometimes simplifies analysis. It is, moreover, not confined to the deformations and forces; coordinates of the general kind can be employed, but this aspect is beyond the scope of this book.

13. The principle of minimum strain energy.

An interesting aspect of the strain-energy and potential-energy methods is revealed by considering an elastic system for which certain of the deflections are prescribed. The physical interpretation of this idea can be appreciated by imagining a structure which is loaded by means of screw jacks at one or more of its joints; the jacks are operated until the deflections of these joints in the lines of action of the jacks have certain prescribed values. Thus, for the simple pin-jointed system shown in fig. II.8 with a vertical screw jack at P, if a prescribed vertical deflection v of P is produced by means of the jack, then v is a constant and $\delta v = 0$.

The strain-energy variation becomes completely identical with the potential-energy variation so that

$$\delta V = \delta U = T_1\,\delta e_1 + T_2\,\delta e_2 = 0 \tag{II.36}$$

Therefore
$$\frac{\partial V}{\partial v} = \frac{\partial U}{\partial v} = 0 \qquad (v \text{ constant})$$

$$\frac{\partial V}{\partial h} = \frac{\partial U}{\partial h} = T_1\frac{\partial e_1}{\partial h} + T_2\frac{\partial e_2}{\partial h} = 0 \tag{II.37}$$

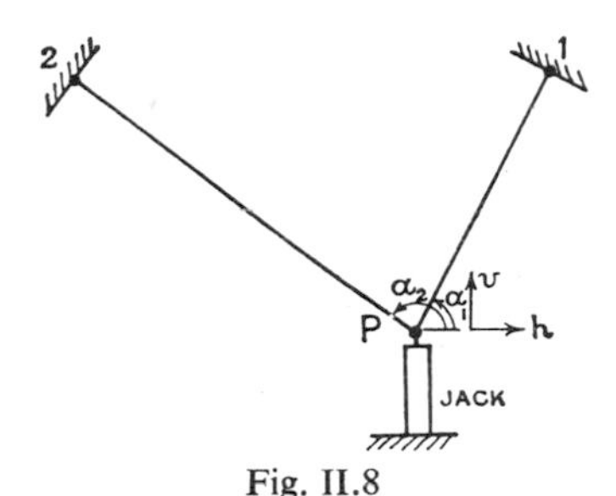

Fig. II.8

Also, by equation (II.3),

$$e_1 = -v\sin\alpha_1 - h\cos\alpha_1$$
$$e_2 = -v\sin\alpha_2 - h\cos\alpha_2$$

and since v is constant

$$\begin{aligned}\delta e_1 &= -\delta h\cos\alpha_1\\ \delta e_2 &= -\delta h\cos\alpha_2\end{aligned} \tag{II.38}$$

If, for the sake of convenience, it is assumed that the elasticity of the members is linear so that $T_1 = b_1 e_1$ and $T_2 = b_2 e_2$, then

$$\frac{dV}{dh} = \frac{dU}{dh} = b_1(v\sin\alpha_1 + h\cos\alpha_1)\cos\alpha_1 + b_2(v\sin\alpha_2 + h\cos\alpha_2)\cos\alpha_2 = 0 \tag{II.39}$$

whence

$$h = \frac{-(b_1\sin 2\alpha_1 + b_2\sin 2\alpha_2)}{2(b_1\cos^2\alpha_1 + b_2\cos^2\alpha_2)}\,v \tag{II.40}$$

It is, moreover, clear that $d^2V/dh^2 = d^2U/dh^2$ is positive because the system is linear and so the equation of equilibrium, equation (II.39), can be interpreted as specifying that if one component of the deflection of **P** is prescribed, the value assumed by the other component is such as to render the strain energy a minimum.

14. More general example of minimum strain energy.

This concept of minimum strain energy is represented much more strikingly by considering certain prescribed deflections of a complicated structure such as that shown in fig. II.9. For example, if a definite vertical deflection of the joint P is introduced by means of, say, a screw jack, and if there are no other external forces acting upon the structure, then

$$\delta V = \delta U = \sum_{1}^{N} T_i \, \delta e_i = 0 \tag{II.41}$$

where N is the number of members in the structure. It is assumed in writing equation (II.41) that the supports of the structure are inelastic, because otherwise terms representing the variation of the strain energy of the supports would have to be introduced. Such terms can be included, however, merely by treating the supports as members of the structure.

Thus, by equation (II.41), since $\delta v_P = 0$,

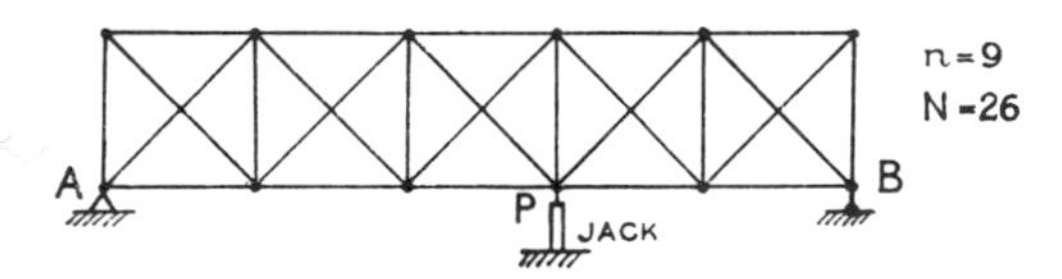

Fig. II.9

$$\begin{aligned}
\frac{\partial V}{\partial v_j} &= \frac{\partial U}{\partial v_j} = \sum_{1}^{N} T_i \frac{\partial e_i}{\partial v_j} = 0 \qquad (j = 1, 2, \ldots, n) \\
\frac{\partial V}{\partial h_j} &= \frac{\partial U}{\partial h_j} = \sum_{1}^{N} T_i \frac{\partial e_i}{\partial h_j} = 0 \qquad (j = 1, 2, \ldots, n) \\
\frac{\partial V}{\partial h_B} &= \frac{\partial U}{\partial h_B} = \sum_{1}^{N} T_i \frac{\partial e_i}{\partial h_B} = 0 \\
\frac{\partial V}{\partial h_P} &= \frac{\partial U}{\partial h_P} = \sum_{1}^{N} T_i \frac{\partial e_i}{\partial h_P} = 0
\end{aligned} \tag{II.42}$$

where n is the number of completely " free " joints and h_B and h_P are the horizontal deflections of B and P, respectively.

Hence, if the structure is linear the equations of equilibrium (II.42) can be interpreted as specifying that if certain prescribed deflections are introduced (one in this instance) the other deflections assume values such that the strain energy of the structure is a minimum. It is this principle which, in the opinion of the author, is the true principle of least work.

15. More general investigation of the potential-energy principle.

After considering the operation of the method of potential energy, it is desirable to examine it in more general terms; also, it is possible in this way to see how the criterion of stability is derived. In order, however, to retain some measure of simplicity, a general conservative system with only one degree of freedom will be considered, for example, a simple non-linear spring such as that shown in fig. I.1.

If a displacement of the system with respect to any arbitrarily chosen position is η*, the potential energy of the displaced system can be expressed as a function $V(\eta)$ of η which can be expanded by Taylor's theorem as follows:

$$V(\eta) = V(0) + V'(0)\eta + V''(0)\frac{\eta^2}{2!} + V'''(0)\frac{\eta^3}{3!} + \ldots \qquad \text{(II.43)}$$

where $V(0)$ is the value of the function when $\eta = 0$, $V'(0)$ is $dV/d\eta$ when $\eta = 0$, $V''(0)$ is $d^2V/d\eta^2$ when $\eta = 0$, etc. As these quantities are constant they can be denoted by c_0, c_1, c_2, etc., respectively so that equation (II.43) can be rewritten as follows:

$$V(\eta) = c_0 + c_1\eta + c_2\frac{\eta^2}{2!} + c_3\frac{\eta^3}{3!} + \ldots \qquad \text{(II.44)}$$

Now, in the event of the system doing work externally, there will be a corresponding decrease in its potential energy, so that if F is the force exerted by the system

$$F\,\delta\eta = -\delta V \qquad \text{(II.45)}$$

or

$$F = -\frac{dV}{d\eta}$$

Therefore, by equation (II.44),

$$F = -\frac{dV}{d\eta} = -\left(c_1 + c_2\eta + c_3\frac{\eta^2}{2!} + \ldots\right) \qquad \text{(II.46)}$$

and constant c_0 which represents the " level " of the potential energy when $\eta = 0$ has disappeared as a result of the differentiation. A position of equilibrium of the system requires, however, that there is no force in action, that is $F = 0$. If, therefore, the configuration of the system represented by $\eta = 0$ is a position of equilibrium, then clearly $c_1 = 0$ and

$$F = -\left(c_2\eta + c_3\frac{\eta^2}{2!} + \ldots\right) \qquad \text{(II.47)}$$

* The symbol η is used here to distinguish from deflections caused by loads or external influences.

Moreover, if a small displacement η is considered such that η^2, η^3, etc., are negligible,

$$F = -c_2\eta \tag{II.48}$$

Thus, for a small displacement η of the system from the position of equilibrium corresponding to $\eta = 0$, the force exerted by the system is given by equation (II.48).

Suppose now that a mass M is associated with the system and is concentrated at the point of action of F. If the mass is given a small displacement η at a time $t = 0$ by an external agency, the subsequent behaviour of the system will be defined by the equation of Newton's second law as follows:

$$M\frac{d^2\eta}{dt^2} = F = -c_2\eta$$

or

$$M\frac{d^2\eta}{dt^2} + c_2\eta = 0 \tag{II.49}$$

The solution of the differential equation (II.49) with respect to time t depends upon the sign of c_2. If c_2 is a positive constant then

$$\eta = A\sin\left\{\sqrt{\left(\frac{c_2}{M}\right)}.t+\phi\right\} \tag{II.50}$$

where A and ϕ are constants which depend upon the initial conditions of the system; for example, $\eta = \delta$ at $t = 0$ and $d\eta/dt = 0$ at $t = 0$ when a definite displacement δ is given to the passive system at $t = 0$. Equation (II.50) is clearly an equation of simple harmonic motion about the position of equilibrium at $\eta = 0$. This means that following any small displacement or disturbance from the position of equilibrium, the system is continually attempting to regain that position of equilibrium, and the equilibrium at $\eta = 0$ is said to be stable.

On the other hand, if c_2 is a negative quantity, the solution of equation (II.49) is of the form

$$\eta = A_1\sinh\sqrt{\left(\frac{c_2}{M}\right)}.t + A_2\cosh\sqrt{\left(\frac{c_2}{M}\right)}.t \tag{II.51}$$

where A_1 and A_2 are constants which depend upon the initial conditions of the system. The hyperbolic form of equation (II.51) indicates that as t increases so η increases, thus the system departs from the configuration of the condition of equilibrium at $\eta = 0$ as the result of a small disturbance, and the condition of equilibrium at $\eta = 0$ is said to be unstable.

In the event of c_2 being zero, $F = 0$ for a small displacement of the system from the position of equilibrium at $\eta = 0$, so that the displacement is maintained and the equilibrium of the system at $\eta = 0$ is said to be neutral.

It must be remembered now that c_2 is $d^2V/d\eta^2$ at $\eta = 0$, the position of equilibrium. Thus the fact that c_2 must be positive for stable equilibrium means that $d^2V/d\eta^2$ is positive when $dV/d\eta = 0$; that is, the potential energy is a minimum for a position of stable equilibrium. If the position is one of unstable equilibrium, however, $dV/d\eta = 0$ but $c_2 = d^2V/d\eta^2$ is negative, meaning that the potential energy is a maximum for a position of unstable equilibrium. Again, in a neutral condition at $\eta = 0$, $dV/d\eta = 0$ and $d^2V/d\eta^2 = 0$, and this means that the potential energy is stationary at a point of contraflexure of the energy-displacement relationship.

The fact that a small displacement of a conservative system in stable equilibrium causes oscillations about the position of equilibrium affords a laboratory approach for investigating stability. The frequency of the oscillations provides an indication of " the degree of stability " of the system. Finally, it is interesting to note that for small displacements, such as η above, of a non-linear elastic system in equilibrium, the resulting behaviour is similar to that of a linear system.

16. Stability analysis.

The study of the stability of systems is a subject in itself, and only the basic aspects can be considered here. It is concerned with determining the limit of stability for small displacements when the natural frequency is zero and the system is neutral. The system shown in fig. II.10 will serve to show the manner in which the limit of stability comes about. The strut CD of length l is rigid and pin-jointed to foundations at D, and it is maintained in the vertical position by a long elastic spring at C having a stiffness b for small deflections.

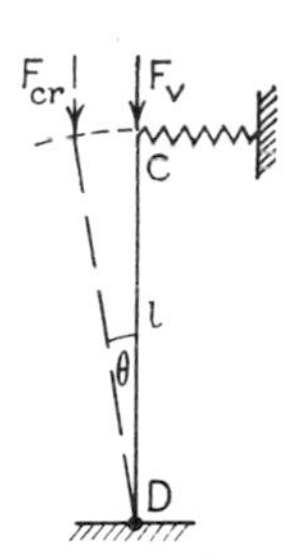

Fig. II.10

If a vertical load F_V is applied to the strut at C then, so long as the strut is truly vertical, there will be no deflection of the system due to the load, and it will be in equilibrium in the vertical configuration. Depending upon the magnitude of the load, however, the equilibrium is stable or unstable or neutral. Thus, imagining the load to be increased slowly from zero, the natural frequency of the oscillations of the system, in stable equilibrium, which would follow a small displacement from the position of equilibrium, will decrease as the load is increased. When at a certain value of the load the natural frequency is zero, the equilibrium is neutral. If the load is increased further, the system becomes unstable, and a small displacement from the vertical configuration (of equilibrium) results in complete departure from that configuration.

In order to determine the magnitude of the load $F_V = F_{cr}$ called the critical load, which renders the system neutral, it is necessary to assume that this load is applied and that a small displacement has been given to the system. If such a displacement causes CD to make a small angle θ with the vertical, the potential energy of the system is

$$V = \tfrac{1}{2}b(l \sin\theta)^2 - F_{cr}\, l(1-\cos\theta) \tag{II.52}$$

where the first term is the strain energy of the spring which, even if it has a non-linear characteristic, can be assumed to be linear for small changes in its length, such as $l \sin\theta$, in accordance with the considerations of § 15; the second term is the potential energy associated with the load, assuming it is gravitational, and the chosen datum of this energy is at the undisplaced position of C.

In the neutral condition

$$\frac{dV}{d\theta} = 0 = bl^2 \sin\theta\cos\theta - F_{cr}\, l \sin\theta \tag{II.53}$$

therefore

$$F_{cr} = bl\cos\theta \tag{II.54}$$

and in the limit as θ approaches zero

$$F_{cr} = bl \tag{II.55}$$

Moreover, in the neutral condition $d^2V/d\theta^2 = 0$ in accordance with the theory given in § 15, and this condition is also satisfied when $F_{cr} = bl$.

If, therefore, $F_V < bl$ the system in the vertical position is in stable equilibrium, but if $F_V > bl$ the equilibrium in this position is unstable. Because the system considered has only one degree of freedom the analysis gives a unique value of the critical load, but in general the analysis yields as many values of the critical load as there are degrees of freedom. Physically, only one of the values is appropriate, however, depending upon the circumstances, and this is usually the smallest value.

17. Conclusion.

Perhaps the most valuable feature and main practical justification of the methods of strain and potential energy is omitted in this Chapter: it is their application for obtaining approximate solutions of complex problems of elastic systems. While the accurate solutions of many such problems would be too laborious for human effort, the energy approach affords considerable simplification. This aspect is considered in Chapter VIII.

III Further Examples of the Use of the Strain-Energy and Potential-Energy Methods

1. Introduction.

This Chapter is mainly concerned with detailed discussion of three examples which provide further illustration of the use of the potential- and strain-energy methods for setting up the equations of equilibrium of statically-indeterminate elastic systems. There, are, however, brief paragraphs on uniqueness and advantages of symmetry also. The first example is included to show how the methods are used when there is " self-straining " due to initial lack of fit of redundant members in the system or uneven expansion due to temperature variations. Self-straining is peculiar to statically-indeterminate systems and cannot occur in a statically-determinate system. The second example includes the non-linearity aspect and is of a type for which the approach embodied in the potential- and strain-energy methods is advantageous.

These examples are also dealt with in Chapter VI by the complementary-energy method in order that the essential features of the two kinds of energy method can be compared.

2. Example 1. Self-strained system.

The plane pin-jointed linearly elastic system ABDG shown in fig. III.1, in which the joints A and G are fixed to rigid abutments, has one redundant and four degrees of freedom of deflection. The members AB, BD, and DG have the same stiffness b, and members BG and AD both have a stiffness $b/\sqrt{2}$. As well as the strains caused by the loading F_{BV}, F_{BH}; F_{DV} and F_{DH} shown, a rise of temperature causes straining of the members. The temperature change and coefficients of expansion are such that if AB, BD, and DG were free to expand, the length of each would increase by λ while the length of BG would increase by $2\sqrt{2}\lambda$ and the length of AD would increase by $\sqrt{2}\lambda$.

For the purpose of analysing the system, the energy equation for a small change in the loading is as follows:

$$\begin{aligned} \delta U &= T_{AB}\,\delta e_{AB} + T_{BD}\,\delta e_{BD} + T_{DG}\,\delta e_{DG} + T_{AD}\,\delta e_{AD} + T_{BG}\,\delta e_{BG} \\ &= F_{BV}\,\delta v_B + F_{BH}\,\delta h_B + F_{DV}\,\delta v_D + F_{DH}\,\delta h_D \end{aligned} \tag{III.1}$$

where positive senses of the deflections v_B, h_B; v_D, h_D of the joints B and D respectively are as shown in fig. III.1.

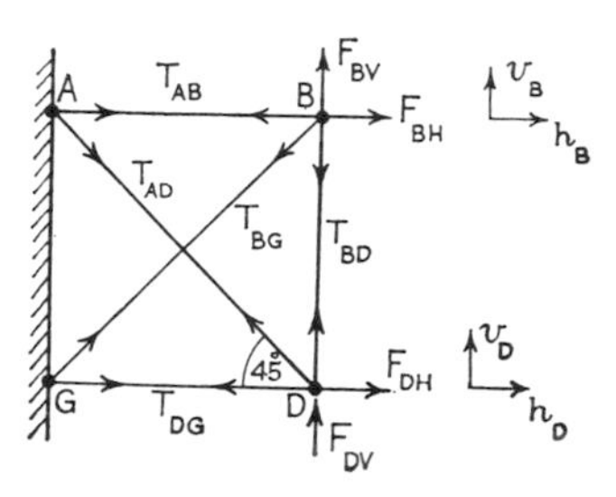

Fig. III.1

The conditions of equilibrium derived from this equation are fourfold, because there are four degrees of freedom and, therefore, four independent components of deflection, thus

$$\begin{aligned}
\frac{\partial U}{\partial v_B} &= T_{AB}\frac{\partial e_{AB}}{\partial v_B} + T_{BD}\frac{\partial e_{BD}}{\partial v_B} + T_{DG}\frac{\partial e_{DG}}{\partial v_B} + T_{AD}\frac{\partial e_{AD}}{\partial v_B} + T_{BG}\frac{\partial e_{BG}}{\partial v_B} = F_{BV} \\
\frac{\partial U}{\partial h_B} &= T_{AB}\frac{\partial e_{AB}}{\partial h_B} + T_{BD}\frac{\partial e_{BD}}{\partial h_B} + T_{DG}\frac{\partial e_{DG}}{\partial h_B} + T_{AD}\frac{\partial e_{AD}}{\partial h_B} + T_{BG}\frac{\partial e_{BG}}{\partial h_B} = F_{BH} \\
\frac{\partial U}{\partial v_D} &= T_{AB}\frac{\partial e_{AB}}{\partial v_D} + T_{BD}\frac{\partial e_{BD}}{\partial v_D} + T_{DG}\frac{\partial e_{DG}}{\partial v_D} + T_{AD}\frac{\partial e_{AD}}{\partial v_D} + T_{BG}\frac{\partial e_{BG}}{\partial v_D} = F_{DV} \\
\frac{\partial U}{\partial h_D} &= T_{AB}\frac{\partial e_{AB}}{\partial h_D} + T_{BD}\frac{\partial e_{BD}}{\partial h_D} + T_{DG}\frac{\partial e_{DG}}{\partial h_D} + T_{AD}\frac{\partial e_{AD}}{\partial h_D} + T_{BG}\frac{\partial e_{BG}}{\partial h_D} = F_{DH}
\end{aligned} \tag{III.2}$$

Now the changes of length e of the members are related to their forces T, the temperature effects, and the deflections of the joints B and D as follows:

$$e_{AB} = \frac{1}{b}T_{AB} + \lambda = h_B$$

$$\therefore \quad T_{AB} = b(h_B - \lambda)$$

$$e_{BD} = \frac{1}{b}T_{BD}+\lambda = v_B - v_D$$

$$\therefore\ T_{BD} = b[(v_B - v_D) - \lambda]$$

$$e_{DG} = \frac{1}{b}T_{DG}+\lambda = h_D$$

$$\therefore\ T_{DG} = b(h_D - \lambda) \qquad \text{(III.3)}$$

$$e_{AD} = \frac{\sqrt{2}}{b}T_{AD}+\sqrt{2}\lambda = \frac{1}{\sqrt{2}}(h_D - v_D)$$

$$\therefore\ T_{AD} = \frac{b}{\sqrt{2}}\left[\frac{1}{\sqrt{2}}(h_D - v_D) - \sqrt{2}\lambda\right]$$

$$e_{BG} = \frac{\sqrt{2}}{b}T_{BG}+2\sqrt{2}\lambda = \frac{1}{\sqrt{2}}(h_B + v_B)$$

$$\therefore\ T_{BG} = \frac{b}{\sqrt{2}}\left[\frac{1}{\sqrt{2}}(h_B + v_B) - 2\sqrt{2}\lambda\right]$$

on the basis that tensile effects in members are positive.

Substitution of the expressions for the forces in the members obtained by the compatibility conditions in equations (III.3) in equations (III.2) and obtaining $\partial e_{AB}/\partial v_B$, etc., from equations (III.3) also, gives the equations of equilibrium in terms of the independent deflections as follows:

$$\frac{\partial U}{\partial v_B} = b[(v_B - v_D) - \lambda] + \frac{b}{2}\left[\frac{1}{\sqrt{2}}(h_B + v_B) - 2\sqrt{2}\lambda\right] = F_{BV}$$

$$\frac{\partial U}{\partial h_B} = b(h_B - \lambda) + \frac{b}{2}\left[\frac{1}{\sqrt{2}}(h_B + v_B) - 2\sqrt{2}\lambda\right] = F_{BH} \qquad \text{(III.4)}$$

$$\frac{\partial U}{\partial v_D} = -b[(v_B - v_D) - \lambda] - \frac{b}{2}\left[\frac{1}{\sqrt{2}}(h_D - v_D) - \sqrt{2}\lambda\right] = F_{DV}$$

$$\frac{\partial U}{\partial h_D} = b(h_D - \lambda) + \frac{b}{2}\left[\frac{1}{\sqrt{2}}(h_D - v_D) - \sqrt{2}\lambda\right] = F_{DH}$$

or

$$\left(1+\frac{1}{2\sqrt{2}}\right)v_B+\frac{1}{2\sqrt{2}}h_B-v_D=\frac{1}{b}F_{BV}+(1+\sqrt{2})\lambda$$

$$\frac{1}{2\sqrt{2}}v_B+\left(1+\frac{1}{2\sqrt{2}}\right)h_B=\frac{1}{b}F_{BH}+(1+\sqrt{2})\lambda$$

$$-v_B+\left(1+\frac{1}{2\sqrt{2}}\right)v_D-\frac{1}{2\sqrt{2}}h_D=\frac{1}{b}F_{DV}-\left(1+\frac{1}{\sqrt{2}}\right)\lambda \qquad \text{(III.5)}$$

$$-\frac{1}{2\sqrt{2}}v_D+\left(1+\frac{1}{2\sqrt{2}}\right)h_D=\frac{1}{b}F_{DH}+\left(1+\frac{1}{\sqrt{2}}\right)\lambda$$

Equations (III.5) are sufficient to enable v_B, h_B, v_D, and h_D to be found in terms of the loads and temperature effects. For example, when $F_{BV} = F_{BH} = F_{DH} = 0$, then

$$v_B=\frac{1{\cdot}69}{b}F_{DV}+1{\cdot}70\lambda$$

$$h_B=-\frac{0{\cdot}44}{b}F_{DV}+1{\cdot}34\lambda$$

$$v_D=\frac{2{\cdot}14}{b}F_{DV}+0{\cdot}30\lambda \qquad \text{(III.6)}$$

$$h_D=\frac{0{\cdot}56}{b}F_{DV}+1{\cdot}34\lambda$$

and now the expressions for the forces in the members can be found by using equations (III.3), thus

$$T_{AB}=b(h_B-\lambda)=-0{\cdot}44\,F_{DV}+0{\cdot}34\,b\lambda \qquad \text{(III.7)}$$

and similarly for T_{BD}, T_{DG}, T_{AD}, and T_{BG}.

It is important to remember that the expressions for the deflections of the joints obtained from equations (III.5) are relative to the positions of B and D when the system is unstrained. The contributions to the deflections due to the loads can be found by putting $\lambda = 0$ in equations (III.6), in this instance of a linear structure.

3. Alternative concept of self-straining.

In the event of the self-straining being due to, say, member BD as the chosen redundant, being initially too short by an amount λ, so that for its fitting into the structure force must be used, resulting in the initial straining of whole system, the procedure of analysis is similar to that described in § 2 above. Equations (III.1) and (III.2) are unchanged and equations (III.3) are changed as follows:

$$e_{AB} = \frac{1}{b}T_{AB} = h_B$$

$$e_{BD} = \frac{1}{b}T_{BD} = v_B - v_D + \lambda$$

$$e_{DG} = \frac{1}{b}T_{DG} = h_D \qquad \text{(III.8)}$$

$$e_{AD} = \frac{\sqrt{2}}{b}T_{AD} = \frac{1}{\sqrt{2}}(h_D - v_D)$$

$$e_{BG} = \frac{\sqrt{2}}{b}T_{BG} = \frac{1}{\sqrt{2}}(h_B + v_B)$$

The remainder of the procedure of analysis is on the lines described above. The deflections of the joints B and D obtained from the analysis will be relative to the positions of these joints when the system is unloaded and the redundant BD is disconnected (so that there is no self-straining). Thus self-straining, however it occurs, makes no essential difference to the application of the strain-energy method. In fact, once the effect of self-straining has been taken into account in the conditions of compatibility, equations (III.2) in this instance, the remainder of the process of analysis is straightforward.

4. Example 2. Non-linear system.

In the hypothetical plane pin-jointed system ABDG shown in fig. III.2, the joints A and G are fixed to rigid abutments, vertical deflection

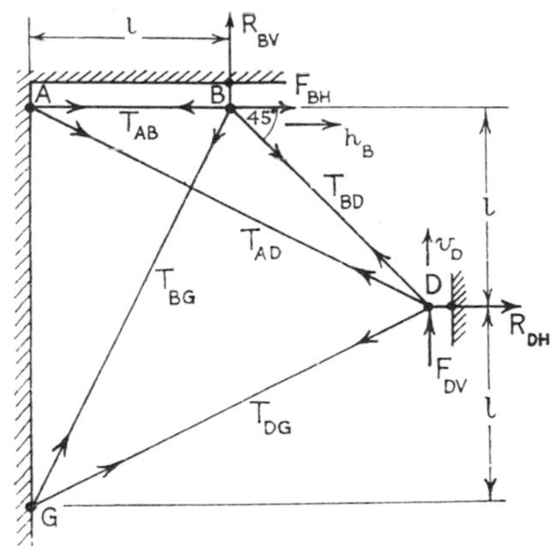

Fig. III.2

of the joint B is prevented and horizontal deflection of the joint D is prevented. The additional constraints at joints B and D reduce the degrees of freedom of the system to two and introduce two additional redundants R_{BV} and R_{DH} respectively, so that as there is one redundant member the system has three redundants in all. All of the members except BD have linear elasticity such that their stiffnesses are inversely proportional to their lengths. The stiffness of member AB is b so that the stiffness of the other linearly elastic members is $b/\sqrt{5}$. The load-deflection characteristic of the non-linear elastic member, when it is in either tension

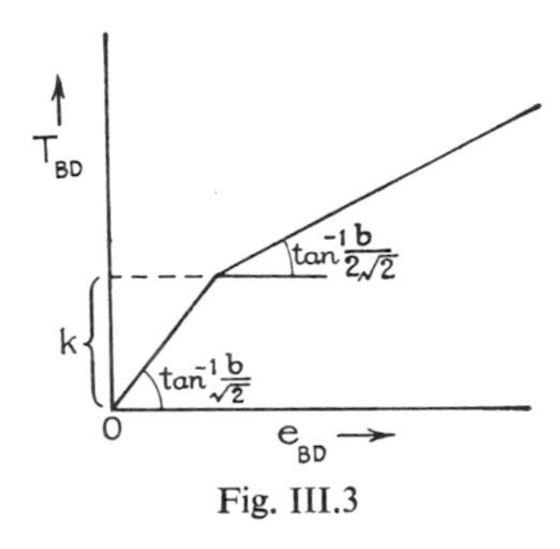

Fig. III.3

or compression, is shown in fig. III.3. Thus, it behaves linearly with a stiffness of $b/\sqrt{2}$ until the force upon it is k, at which point its slope changes to $b/(2\sqrt{2})$. The system is loaded by forces F_{BH} and F_{DV} at B and D, respectively, and the deflections of these joints are denoted by h_B and v_D.

For the purpose of analysing this system the potential-energy form will be used, and the equation of the variation of the potential energy of the loaded system in equilibrium is as follows:

$$\delta V = T_{AB}\,\delta e_{AB} + T_{BD}\,\delta e_{BD} + T_{AD}\,\delta e_{AD} + T_{BG}\,\delta e_{BG} + T_{DG}\,\delta e_{DG} - F_{BH}\,\delta h_B - F_{DV}\,\delta v_D = 0 \tag{III.9}$$

and the conditions of equilibrium derived from this equation are

$$\frac{\partial V}{\partial h_B} = T_{AB}\frac{\partial e_{AB}}{\partial h_B} + T_{BD}\frac{\partial e_{BD}}{\partial h_B} + T_{AD}\frac{\partial e_{AD}}{\partial h_B} + T_{BG}\frac{\partial e_{BG}}{\partial h_B} + T_{DG}\frac{\partial e_{DG}}{\partial h_B} - F_{BH} = 0$$

$$\frac{\partial V}{\partial v_D} = T_{AB}\frac{\partial e_{AB}}{\partial v_D} + T_{BD}\frac{\partial e_{BD}}{\partial v_D} + T_{AD}\frac{\partial e_{AD}}{\partial v_D} + T_{BG}\frac{\partial e_{BG}}{\partial v_D} + T_{DG}\frac{\partial e_{DG}}{\partial v_D} - F_{DV} = 0 \tag{III.10}$$

In order to express the equations of equilibrium in terms of the independent deflections h_B and v_D, the conditions of compatibility and the load-deflection characteristics of the members must be introduced. Thus, assuming tensile effects in members are positive,

$$
\begin{aligned}
e_{AB} &= h_B, & \therefore\ T_{AB} &= be_{AB} = bh_B \\
e_{BD} &= -\frac{1}{\sqrt{2}}h_B - \frac{1}{\sqrt{2}}v_D, & \therefore\ T_{BD} &= \frac{b}{2\sqrt{2}}(e_{BD} \pm e_k) = \\
& & & \frac{b}{4}[-(h_B+v_D) \pm \sqrt{2}e_k] \\
e_{AD} &= -\frac{1}{\sqrt{5}}v_D, & \therefore\ T_{AD} &= \frac{b}{\sqrt{5}}e_{AD} = -\frac{b}{5}v_D \\
e_{BG} &= \frac{1}{\sqrt{5}}h_B, & \therefore\ T_{BG} &= \frac{b}{\sqrt{5}}e_{BG} = \frac{b}{5}h_B \\
e_{DG} &= \frac{1}{\sqrt{5}}v_D, & \therefore\ T_{DG} &= \frac{b}{\sqrt{5}}e_{DG} = \frac{b}{5}v_D
\end{aligned}
\tag{III.11}
$$

In writing $T_{BD} = [b/(2\sqrt{2})]\,(e_{BD} \pm e_k)$ it is assumed that $e_{BD} > e_k$ numerically, that is, that $T_{BD} > k$: otherwise, when $T_{BD} \leqslant k$, $T_{BD} = (b/\sqrt{2})e_{BD}$ and the system is linear. It is, moreover, necessary to write $\pm e_k$ in general because the sign of e_k is not automatically taken into account: thus if BD is likely to be in compression, it is necessary to use the form $T_{BD} = [b/(2\sqrt{2})]\,(e_{BD} - e_k)$ in the analysis.

Substitution of equations (III.11) in equations (III.10) gives the following final equations of equilibrium when $T_{BD} > k$ numerically:

$$
\begin{aligned}
-\frac{b}{4\sqrt{2}}[-(h_B+v_D) \pm \sqrt{2}e_k] + b\left(1+\frac{1}{5\sqrt{5}}\right)h_B &= F_{BH} \\
-\frac{b}{4\sqrt{2}}[-(h_B+v_D) \pm \sqrt{2}e_k] + \frac{2}{5\sqrt{5}}b\,v_D &= F_{DV}
\end{aligned}
\tag{III.12}
$$

If $F_{DV} = +\,10k$ and $F_{BH} = 0$, since $e_k = (\sqrt{2}/b)k$ these equations become

$$
\begin{aligned}
1{\cdot}27\,bh_B + 0{\cdot}18\,bv_D + 0{\cdot}35\,k &= 0 \\
0{\cdot}18\,bh_B + 0{\cdot}36\,bv_D + 0{\cdot}35\,k &= 10k
\end{aligned}
\tag{III.13}
$$

on the assumption that T_{BD} is compressive, so that the minus sign is used for e_k within the bracket in equations (III.12). Solution of equations (III.13) yields

$$h_B = -4{\cdot}27\frac{k}{b} \quad : \quad v_D = 29{\cdot}25\frac{k}{b} \tag{III.14}$$

therefore

$$T_{BD} = -6{\cdot}75\,k$$

which is in accordance with the assumptions that $T_{BD} > k$ numerically and is compressive. Had the solution not been in accordance with these assumptions it would have been necessary to explore the alternatives of T_{BD} being tensile and $< k$ numerically, as appropriate.

It will be noted that this method of dealing with this problem is more convenient than that using complementary energy (demonstrated in Chapter VI, § 4), mainly because there are only two independent deflection components whereas there are three redundants. After finding the deflections it is, of course, easy to find the force in each member by means of equations (III.11).

5. Uniqueness of solutions.

The previous example and that of Chapter II, § 11, and Chapter V, § 13, give some indication of the analytical difficulties of dealing with non-linear elastic systems. In general, the signs of the various terms look after themselves* only for certain kinds of elasticity, for example linear elasticity, because then $T = be$ and the signs of T and e correspond. In the kind of non-linear elasticity introduced above in respect of the member BD, a change of sign of e_{BD} does not lead to a correct solution unless suitable changes in sign are imposed on the constant term. This feature sometimes necessitates the exploration of alternative combinations of signs in order to find the solution which is in accordance with the physical facts. Again, if the elasticity of a member is such that $T = be^2$ there is no correspondence between the signs of T and e; it is necessary to write $T = \pm be^2$ and explore the two alternatives, unless it is quite clear by inspection of the problem which sign should be used. On the other hand, elasticity of the kind $T = be^3$ does not suffer from this analytical drawback. In fact, it can be said in general that when elasticity is of the general form $T = be^n$, the difficulty under discussion does not arise when n is odd. Further generalization concerning this aspect is unfortunately not possible.

6. Advantages of symmetry.

A very important aspect in analysis, which is not illustrated in the previous examples, is that whereby advantage is taken of symmetry to reduce the number of variables involved. Thus in the system shown in fig. III.4, so long as the loading is vertical (symmetrical) and the members are symmetrical geometrically and elastically about the vertical centre line, there can be no horizontal components of joint deflection, so that the number of unknown deflections is immediately reduced from four to

* It is, perhaps, one reason for the popular appeal of energy methods that for linear systems, which are frequently encountered, there is no need to trouble about signs.

two. Similarly for symmetrical linear systems, it is frequently advantageous to split up systems of loading into symmetrical and skew-symmetrical components and consider each separately (see Chapter IV, § 15). In this

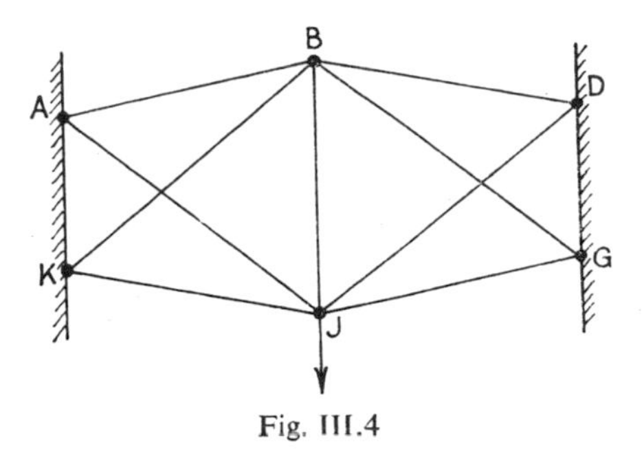

Fig. III.4

way, although the analysis is performed in parts, the number of simultaneous equations to be solved for any part of the analysis is usually significantly less than that involved if the orthodox procedure is adopted.

IV The Principle of Virtual Work

1. Introduction.

The principle of virtual work, a principle used implicitly in mechanics as long ago as the thirteenth century,* is primarily a means of deriving conditions of equilibrium. It follows from the application of the law of conservation of energy to the work quantities which are the consequence of small, arbitrary, compatible displacements of a conservative statical system which is in stable equilibrium. It can be considered as a direct application of the principle of stationary potential energy if the arbitrary displacements are infinitesimally small: however, it is shown in Chapter II, § 15, that the condition for potential energy to be stationary, i.e. $\delta V = 0$, is in fact also a manifestation of the law of conservation of energy. The principle of virtual work is useful in engineering science in the form appropriate for small but finite arbitrary imaginary displacements of systems in equilibrium and is of immense value in the study of theory of structures. It is the basis of the method of complementary energy for deriving expressions for deflections of linear and non-linear elastic systems.

2. Derivation of the principle.

The principle of virtual work can be proved in its own right in a simple way. Suppose a number of forces $F_1, F_2, \ldots, F_N$ are acting at a point P and their resultant is F_R as shown in fig. IV.1. If P moves through an infinitesimally small distance δs_R under the influence of the forces, the work equation is

$$F_R \delta s_R = F_1 \delta s_1 + F_2 \delta s_2 + \ldots + F_N \delta s_N \qquad \text{(IV.1)}$$

by the law of conservation of energy, where $\delta s_1, \delta s_2, \ldots, \delta s_N$ are the movements in the lines of action of $F_1, F_2, \ldots, F_N$ caused by δs_R. There is, moreover, no reason why the displacement s_R should not be

* The principle of virtual work has been traced to Jean Bernoulli's letter of 26th January, 1717, to Varignon but it was used implicitly by Jordanus of Nemore in the thirteenth century.

finite so long as the forces are constant in magnitude and direction, in which case

$$F_R s_R = F_1 s_1 + F_2 s_2 + \ldots + F_N s_N \tag{IV.2}$$

Yet another form is possible if it is supposed that the displacement δs_R in equation (IV.1) takes place during an interval of time δt. Dividing equation (IV.1) throughout by δt gives

$$F_R \frac{ds_R}{dt} = F_1 \frac{ds_1}{dt} + F_2 \frac{ds_2}{dt} + \ldots + F_N \frac{ds_N}{dt}$$

or

$$F_R u_R = F_1 u_1 + F_2 u_2 + \ldots + F_N u_N \tag{IV.3}$$

where $u_1, u_2, \ldots, u_N$ are the instantaneous velocities along the lines of action of $F_1, F_2, \ldots, F_N$, respectively when P has an instantaneous velocity u_R in the line of action of the resultant force.

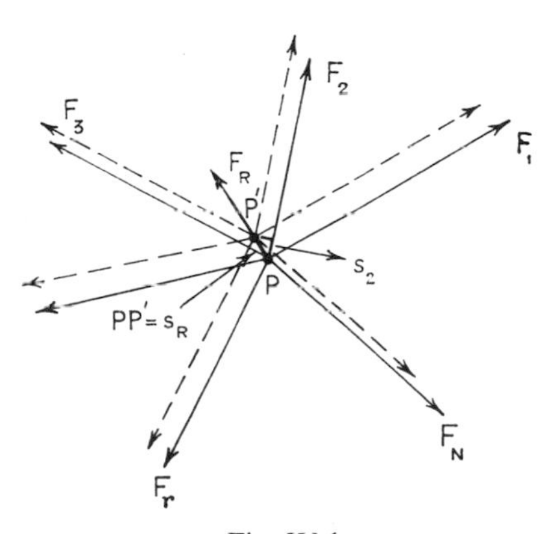

Fig. IV.1

When, however, the forces $F_1, F_2, \ldots, F_N$ are in equilibrium and there is no force to cause movement of P, then if P is imagined to be displaced by, say, the temporary action of an external agency, the following equations of imaginary or virtual work are obtained:

$$F_1 \delta s_1 + F_2 \delta s_2 + \ldots + F_N \delta s_N = 0 \tag{IV.4}$$

or

$$F_1 s_1 + F_2 s_2 + \ldots + F_N s_N = 0 \tag{IV.5}$$

or

$$F_1 u_1 + F_2 u_2 + \ldots + F_N u_N = 0 \tag{IV.6}$$

Equation (IV.6) expresses the form known as the principle of virtual velocities. It is important to note that the word " virtual " is introduced because an imaginary (but physically possible) state of affairs is considered.

Moreover, because $F_R = 0$, the direction of the imaginary displacement of P (δs_R or s_R) is unimportant; the displacements in the directions of the lines of action of the forces, being compatible with the displacement of P, are the resolved components of the displacement of P in these directions, respectively.

3. Example of the use of virtual work for analysing statically-determinate systems.

One of the simplest examples of the application of the principle of virtual work is its use for finding the forces in the members of the pin-jointed statically-determinate structure shown in fig. IV.2. If the members are assumed to be rigid there is no doubt whatever that virtual work is being used and not real work. If the members of this system are elastic, however, it can be treated as well by the method of real work or strain energy as in Chapter II, § 2. It will be observed that the real-work procedure is identical in the mathematical sense to that used below, because the elastic deformation of the members is assumed to have a negligible effect upon the geometry of the structure. Thus when a structure is statically-determinate and does not distort significantly under load, the forces in the members are independent of elasticity.

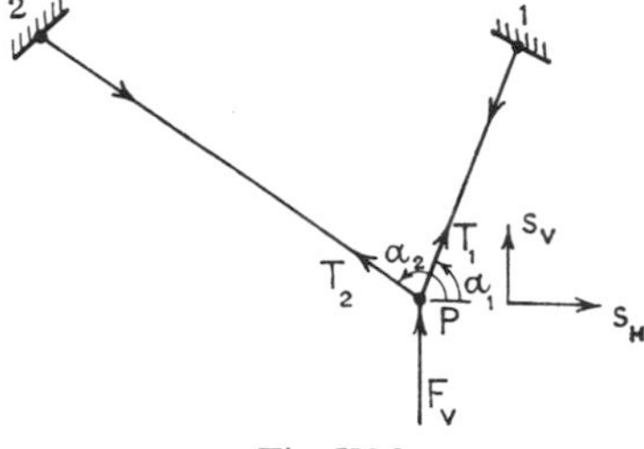

Fig. IV.2

If, then, the joint P is imagined to be displaced in an arbitrary manner described by the components δs_V in the direction of F_V and δs_H at right angles to F_V, because P is in equilibrium,

$$0\,\delta s_H + F_V\,\delta s_V + T_1\,\delta s_1 + T_2\,\delta s_2 = 0 \tag{IV.7}$$

assuming that the forces T_1 and T_2 are tensile, as shown in fig. IV.2, and that the displacements in the directions of the forces, δs_1 and δs_2, are in the sense of shortening the members, respectively, so that work would be done by each force. For compatibility of the virtual displacements, however,

$$\begin{aligned} \delta s_1 &= \delta s_V \sin\alpha_1 + \delta s_H \cos\alpha_1 \\ \delta s_2 &= \delta s_V \sin\alpha_2 + \delta s_H \cos\alpha_2 \end{aligned} \tag{IV.8}$$

and substituting these expressions in equation (IV.7) gives

$$F_V\,\delta s_V + (T_1 \sin\alpha_1 + T_2 \sin\alpha_2)\delta s_V + (T_1 \cos\alpha_1 + T_2 \cos\alpha_2)\delta s_H = 0$$

Therefore because δs_V and δs_H are geometrically independent,

$$F_V + T_1 \sin\alpha_1 + T_2 \sin\alpha_2 = 0 \qquad \text{(IV.9)}$$

$$T_1 \cos\alpha_1 + T_2 \cos\alpha_2 = 0$$

which are the equations of equilibrium of P and are identical to equations (II.5). They are, of course, sufficient to enable T_1 and T_2 to be found. It should be noted that an arbitrary virtual displacement of P with components δs_V and δs_H is chosen for generality in order to enable equations of equilibrium in the two chosen directions to be obtained. If desired, separate virtual displacements δs_V and δs_H could have been considered to obtain equations (IV.9) and, in the event of P being a joint in a space structure, the general virtual displacement would have three components, e.g. δs_V, δs_H and δs_Z.

4. Example of the use of the principle of virtual velocities.

The use of the principle in the form of virtual velocities is readily illustrated by reference to a simple mechanism such as the slider-crank

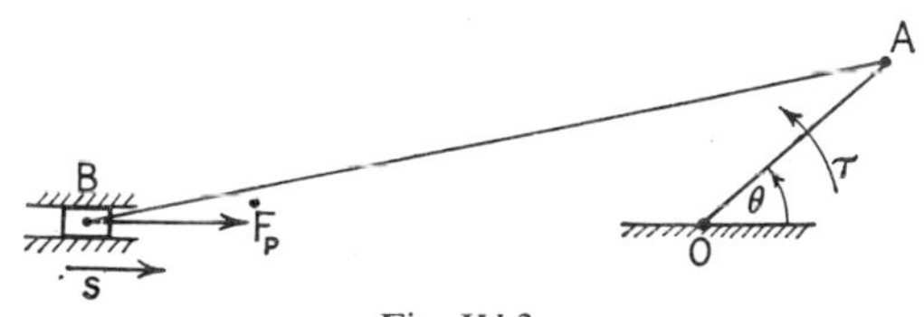

Fig. IV.3

mechanism shown in fig. IV.3. If it is desired to find the torque τ at the crankshaft which is in equilibrium with a force F_P on the piston, by the principle of virtual velocities, assuming negligible inertia effects,

$$F_P \frac{ds}{dt} - \tau \frac{d\theta}{dt} = 0 \qquad \text{(IV.10)}$$

and putting $ds/dt = u_P$ and $d\theta/dt = \omega$

$$F_P u_P - \tau\omega = 0$$

so that

$$\tau = F_P \frac{u_P}{\omega} \qquad \text{(IV.11)}$$

Equation (IV.10) is written on the basis that F_P is doing work upon a load torque of τ at the crankshaft. Thus, if the relative velocities within the mechanism have been found by means of a velocity diagram or otherwise, the torque at the crankshaft can be found immediately. The validity of writing equation (IV.10) directly, instead of considering the conditions at the crosshead B and crankpin A and combining them, is shown immediately by application of the law of conservation of energy.

5. The use of finite virtual displacements.

In the examples considered above, infinitesimally-small arbitrary virtual displacements are used but, as proposed in § 2, finite arbitrary virtual displacements can be considered so long as such displacements would not cause a significant change in the geometry of the system in the loaded condition if they actually occurred. In other words, so long as the geometrical relationships for the compatibility of finite virtual displacements are the same as if the displacements were infinitesimally small, the use of such finite virtual displacements is permissible.

In terms of finite virtual displacements the virtual-work equation (IV.7) is as follows:

$$0\, s_H + F_V\, s_V + T_1\, s_1 + T_2\, s_2 = 0 \qquad \text{(IV.12)}$$

where s_V, s_1 and s_2 satisfy the compatibility conditions:

$$\begin{aligned} s_1 &= s_V \sin\alpha_1 + s_H \cos\alpha_1 \\ s_2 &= s_V \sin\alpha_2 + s_H \cos\alpha_2 \end{aligned} \qquad \text{(IV.13)}$$

which are essentially the same as equations (IV.8). Thus the magnitudes of the finite virtual displacements s_V and s_H upon which s_1 and s_2 depend are insufficient to cause significant change in the angles α_1 and α_2.

6. Change of notation for virtual work.

In the particular example to which virtual-work equations (IV.7) and (IV.12) apply the virtual displacements s_1 and s_2 represent virtual changes in length of the members, say e_1' and e_2'. Therefore putting $s_V = v'$ and $s_H = h'$ equation (IV.12) can be rewritten

$$0\, h' + F_V\, v' + T_1\, e_1' + T_2\, e_2' = 0 \qquad \text{(IV.14)}$$

where

$$\begin{aligned} e_1' &= v' \sin\alpha_1 + h' \cos\alpha_1 \\ e_2' &= v' \sin\alpha_2 + h' \cos\alpha_2 \end{aligned} \qquad \text{(IV.15)}$$

and are clearly positive for virtual shortening of the members. It is, however, preferable for subsequent analysis to rewrite equation (IV.14) in such a way that the virtual changes in length of the members are positive when they imply lengthening (as could be caused by tensile forces assumed). If this is done equation (IV.14) becomes

$$F_V\, v' = T_1\, e_1' + T_2\, e_2' \qquad \text{(IV.16)}$$

where now

$$\begin{aligned} e_1' &= -v' \sin\alpha_1 - h' \cos\alpha_1 \\ e_2' &= -v' \sin\alpha_2 - h' \cos\alpha_2 \end{aligned} \qquad \text{(IV.17)}$$

7. Choice of particular virtual displacements for elastic systems.

In the event of the members of the structure shown in fig. IV.2 being elastic instead of rigid, a load F_V will cause deflections v and h of P, and corresponding changes of length e_1 and e_2 of the members. So long as v and h are sufficiently small that the changes which they cause in the angles α_1 and α_2 of the members are insignificant, then it is clearly possible to use a system of virtual displacements which is identical to the actual displacements of the system; that is, to imagine compatible displacements v, h, e_1 and e_2 of the loaded system whereby P is imagined to move to a position in which it would be actually $2v$ and $2h$ from its position when the system is unloaded. Therefore the virtual-work equation including virtual displacements equal to the actual deflections of the system is

$$0h + F_V v = T_1 e_1 + T_2 e_2 \qquad \text{(IV.18)}$$

where v, h, e_1 and e_2 satisfy the compatibility conditions

$$\begin{aligned} e_1 &= -v \sin\alpha_1 - h \cos\alpha_1 \\ e_2 &= -v \sin\alpha_2 - h \cos\alpha_2 \end{aligned} \qquad \text{(IV.19)}$$

In general, for elastic structures, virtual displacements equal to and superimposed upon the deflections of the joints due to the applied loads

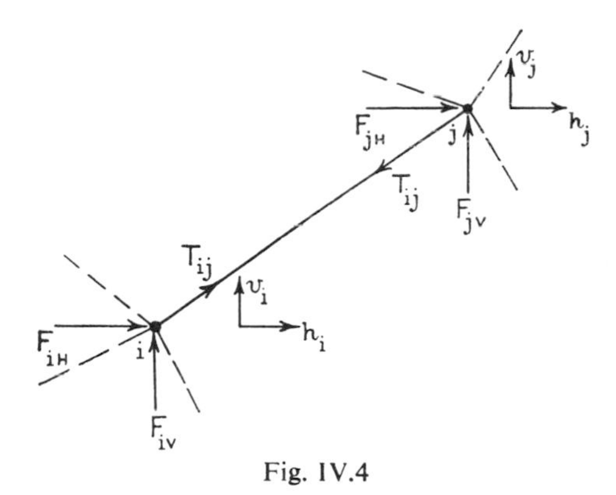

Fig. IV.4

are permissible, provided that the latter do not cause a significant change in the geometry of the structure. By combining the equations of virtual work in terms of such virtual displacements for every joint, an equation of the following kind is obtained*:

$$\sum F_V v + \sum F_H h = \sum T e \qquad \text{(IV.20)}$$

where the forces T include the forces in elastic supports as well as in the members. A similar equation can, of course, be obtained for elastic systems other than pin-jointed structures, for which the elastic deformations do not alter the geometry significantly.

Virtual-work equations of the kind (IV.18) and (IV.20) are of direct value in the theory of elastic systems only when there is a single applied load. In such an event the deflection of the point of application of the load in its line of action can be expressed directly; for example, by equation (IV.18),

$$v = \frac{1}{F_V}(T_1 e_1 + T_2 e_2) \qquad \text{(IV.21)}$$

where T_1, e_1, T_2, and e_2 can be expressed in terms of F_V.

The main value of the form of the principle of virtual work considered in this section is that it indicates that complementary energy is " conserved " regardless of whether the elasticity of the system is linear or non-linear as shown in Chapter V, § 2.

8. Use of virtual work for finding deflections of elastic systems.

The method of virtual work using virtual displacements which are equal to actual deflections can, however, be adopted for finding the

* Some indication that this is so can be obtained by considering an elastic member connecting the ith and the jth joint of a pin-jointed structure as shown in fig. IV.4. If the loads applied at these joints are F_{iV}, F_{iH}; F_{jV}, F_{jH}, respectively, and together with loads at other joints produce deflections v_i, h_i; v_j, h_j, respectively, the virtual-work equations for the joints, using virtual displacements equal to the actual deflections, will be of the form

$$F_{iV} v_i + F_{iH} h_i + \ldots + T_{ij}(e_{ij})_i + \ldots = 0$$

and

$$F_{jV} v_j + F_{jH} h_j + \ldots + T_{ij}(e_{ij})_j + \ldots = 0$$

where T_{ij} is the force in the member which connects the two joints and $(e_{ij})_i$ is the deflection at the joint i in the line of this member and $(e_{ij})_j$ is the deflection at j in the same line. If the structure has n joints, there are clearly n pairs of equations such as these, and by adding them an equation of virtual work of the following form is obtained:

$$\ldots + F_{iV} v_i + F_{iH} h_i + F_{jV} v_j + F_{jH} h_j + \ldots + \\ + T_{ij}[(e_{ij})_i + (e_{ij})_j] + \ldots = 0$$

and each member will contribute a term such as that shown for T_{ij}. Now $[(e_{ij})_i + (e_{ij})_j]$ represents e_{ij}, the virtual change in the length of the member, being equal to the actual change in length caused by the loading. Therefore, ascribing to T_{ij} and e_{ij} consistent signs, in the manner described in § 6 above, the equation of virtual work becomes

$$\Sigma F_V v + \Sigma F_H h = \ldots + T_{ij} e_{ij} + \ldots = \Sigma T e \quad \text{(equation IV.20)}$$

deflection of any point of an elastic system in any direction. The way in which this is done is most easily demonstrated by means of a simple example, and the pin-jointed system shown in fig. IV.5 is useful for the purpose. Suppose the deflection h due to the load F_V is required, having found T_1 and T_2 by the conditions of equilibrium, and hence e_1 and e_2 with the aid of the load-deflection characteristics of the members. It is

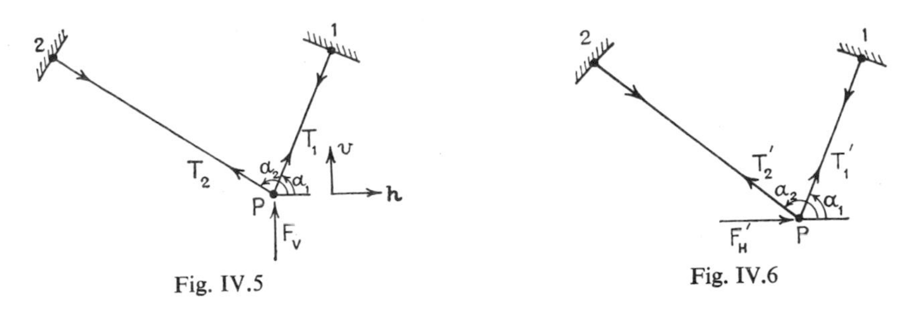

Fig. IV.5

Fig. IV.6

necessary to determine the forces in the members T_1' and T_2', say, due to an arbitrary load F_H' applied at P in the line of the deflection h, as shown in fig. IV.6. The system of forces T_1', T_2', and F_H' is an arbitrary system in equilibrium, and the next step is to consider the virtual work of this system when compatible virtual displacements are introduced which are equal to v, h, e_1, and e_2 due to the load F_V. The relevant equation of virtual work is, therefore,

$$0\,v + F_H'\,h = T_1'\,e_1 + T_2'\,e_2 \qquad \text{(IV.22)}$$

so that

$$h = \frac{1}{F_H'}(T_1'\,e_1 + T_2'\,e_2) \qquad \text{(IV.23)}$$

Thus, if the members have, say, linear elasticity such that $e_1 = a_1 T_1$ and $e_2 = a_2 T_2$, then since by the conditions of equilibrium of P,

$$\left.\begin{aligned} T_1 &= -F_V \frac{\cos\alpha_2}{\sin\alpha_1\cos\alpha_2 - \cos\alpha_1\sin\alpha_2} \\ T_2 &= F_V \frac{\cos\alpha_1}{\sin\alpha_1\cos\alpha_2 - \cos\alpha_1\sin\alpha_2} \end{aligned}\right\} \qquad \text{(IV.24)}$$

it follows that

$$\left.\begin{aligned} e_1 &= -a_1 F_V \frac{\cos\alpha_2}{\sin\alpha_1\cos\alpha_2 - \cos\alpha_1\sin\alpha_2} \\ e_2 &= a_2 F_V \frac{\cos\alpha_1}{\sin\alpha_1\cos\alpha_2 - \cos\alpha_1\sin\alpha_2} \end{aligned}\right\} \qquad \text{(IV.25)}$$

Again, by the conditions of equilibrium of P,

$$T_1' = F_H' \frac{\sin\alpha_2}{\sin\alpha_1\cos\alpha_2 - \cos\alpha_1\sin\alpha_2}$$

$$T_2' = -F_H' \frac{\sin\alpha_1}{\sin\alpha_1\cos\alpha_2 - \cos\alpha_1\sin\alpha_2} \tag{IV.26}$$

Substitution from equations (IV.25) and (IV.26) in equation (IV.23) gives

$$h = -F_V \frac{a_1\sin\alpha_2\cos\alpha_2 + a_2\sin\alpha_1\cos\alpha_1}{(\sin\alpha_1\cos\alpha_2 - \cos\alpha_1\sin\alpha_2)^2} \tag{IV.27}$$

The basis of this method of finding deflections is, therefore, the virtual work of an appropriate arbitrary system of forces due to virtual displacements which are equal to the deflections which are actually produced by the loading. The method is, of course, completely dependent on actual deflections being small enough to have no significant effect upon the geometry of the system, because only then can identical virtual displacements be considered, as explained above.

9. Use of virtual work as an aid to the analysis of statically-indeterminate systems.

This method of using the principle of virtual work for finding deflections is useful in connection with the analysis of elastic statically-indeterminate or redundant systems. If the pin-jointed structure shown

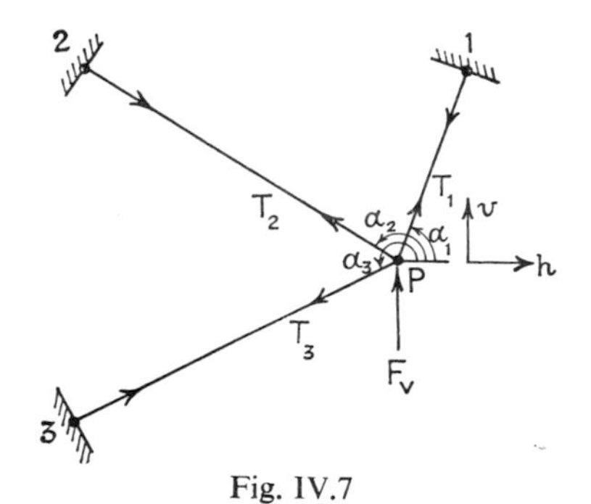

Fig. IV.7

in fig. IV.5 has a redundant member as shown in fig. IV.7, an expression for the force T_3 in this member due any loading at P can be found by considering the condition for the deflection of the statically-determinate system in the line of the redundant member to be compatible with the deflection of the member itself.

Thus, if the load at P is F_V, so far as the statically-determinate system is concerned it is subjected to forces F_V and T_3 as shown in fig. IV.8 (assuming the redundant member is in tension). By the conditions of equilibrium of P the forces in the members are

$$T_1 = -\frac{T_3(\cos\alpha_2 \sin\alpha_3 - \sin\alpha_2 \cos\alpha_3) + F_V \cos\alpha_2}{\sin\alpha_1 \cos\alpha_2 - \cos\alpha_1 \sin\alpha_2}$$

$$T_2 = \frac{T_3(\cos\alpha_1 \sin\alpha_3 - \sin\alpha_1 \cos\alpha_3) + F_V \cos\alpha_1}{\sin\alpha_1 \cos\alpha_2 - \cos\alpha_1 \sin\alpha_2} \tag{IV.28}$$

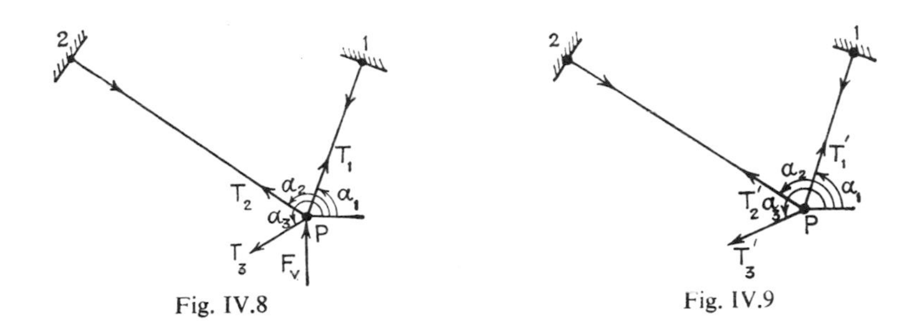

Fig. IV.8 Fig. IV.9

so that if the members have linear elasticity with flexibilities a_1 and a_2

$$e_1 = -a_1 \frac{T_3(\cos\alpha_2 \sin\alpha_3 - \sin\alpha_2 \cos\alpha_3) + F_V \cos\alpha_2}{\sin\alpha_1 \cos\alpha_2 - \cos\alpha_1 \sin\alpha_2}$$

$$e_2 = a_2 \frac{T_3(\cos\alpha_1 \sin\alpha_3 - \sin\alpha_1 \cos\alpha_3) + F_V \cos\alpha_1}{\sin\alpha_1 \cos\alpha_2 - \cos\alpha_1 \sin\alpha_2} \tag{IV.29}$$

In order to use equations (IV.29) to find an expression for the deflection of the statically-determinate system in the line of the redundant member, it is necessary to consider a suitable arbitrary system of forces in equilibrium as shown in fig. IV.9. By the conditions of equilibrium of P, therefore,

$$T_1' = -T_3' \frac{\cos\alpha_2 \sin\alpha_3 - \sin\alpha_2 \cos\alpha_3}{\sin\alpha_1 \cos\alpha_2 - \cos\alpha_1 \sin\alpha_2}$$

$$T_2' = T_3' \frac{\cos\alpha_1 \sin\alpha_3 - \sin\alpha_1 \cos\alpha_3}{\sin\alpha_1 \cos\alpha_2 - \cos\alpha_1 \sin\alpha_2} \tag{IV.30}$$

Now the virtual work of this system of forces in equilibrium using virtual displacements equal to the deflections caused by F_V is as follows:

$$T_3' e_3 = T_1' e_1 + T_2' e_2 \tag{IV.31}$$

Substitution from equations (IV.29) and (IV.30) gives

$$e_3 = \frac{\begin{array}{l} a_1(\cos\alpha_2 \sin\alpha_3 - \sin\alpha_2 \cos\alpha_3)\,[T_3(\cos\alpha_2 \sin\alpha_3 - \sin\alpha_2 \cos\alpha_3) + F_V \cos\alpha_2] \\ \quad + a_2(\cos\alpha_1 \sin\alpha_3 - \sin\alpha_1 \cos\alpha_3)\,[T_3(\cos\alpha_1 \sin\alpha_3 - \sin\alpha_1 \cos\alpha_3) + F_V \cos\alpha_1] \end{array}}{(\sin\alpha_1 \cos\alpha_2 - \cos\alpha_1 \sin\alpha_2)^2} \qquad \text{(IV.32)}$$

as the deflection of P of the statically-determinate system in the line of action and direction of T_3 due to loads F_V and T_3. This means that l_3, the length of the line of the redundant member in the unloaded structure, is shortened by e_3 so that

$$l_3' = l_3 - e_3 \qquad \text{(IV.33)}$$

But the force T_3 is due to the redundant member and, as it is assumed to be in tension, in accordance with the sense of the load T_3 shown in fig. IV.8, its strained length is

$$l_3' = l_3 + a_3 T_3 \qquad \text{(IV.34)}$$

if the elasticity of the member is linear of flexibility a_3 and its original length is l_3.

Now l_3' in equation (IV.34) must be the same as the length l_3' given by equation (IV.33), because the member is actually part of the structure. Therefore, by equations (IV.33) and (IV.34),

$$l_3 - e_3 = l_3 + a_3 T_3$$

or

$$e_3 + a_3 T_3 = 0 \qquad \text{(IV.35)}$$

which is the condition for the strains of the statically-determinate system and the redundant member to be compatible. Therefore, substituting for e_3 from equation (IV.32), the following equation in T_3 is obtained:*

$$\frac{\begin{array}{l} a_1(\cos\alpha_2 \sin\alpha_3 - \sin\alpha_2 \cos\alpha_3)\,[T_3(\cos\alpha_2 \sin\alpha_3 - \sin\alpha_2 \cos\alpha_3) + F_V \cos\alpha_2] \\ \quad + a_2(\cos\alpha_1 \sin\alpha_3 - \sin\alpha_1 \cos\alpha_3)\,[T_3(\cos\alpha_1 \sin\alpha_3 - \sin\alpha_1 \cos\alpha_3) + F_V \cos\alpha_1] \end{array}}{(\sin\alpha_1 \cos\alpha_2 - \cos\alpha_1 \sin\alpha_2)^2} + a_3 T_3 = 0 \qquad \text{(IV.36)}$$

so that T_3 and hence T_1 and T_2 can be found.

10. More than one redundant member.

If there are two redundant members, as shown in fig. IV.10, equations (IV.28), and therefore equations (IV.29), must be modified to include terms for the force T_4 in the second redundant member and, besides finding e_3 for the statically-determinate system as above, e_4 must be

* See also equation (V.26)

found as well by considering the virtual work of a second arbitrary system of forces in equilibrium T_4'', T_1'', and T_2''. Then, two equations for the compatibility of strains are obtained as follows:

$$\begin{aligned} e_3 + a_3 T_3 &= 0 \\ e_4 + a_4 T_4 &= 0 \end{aligned} \qquad \text{(IV.37)}$$

if e_3 as given by equation (IV.32) is modified to include the T_4 load terms.

This method of finding equations for the forces in the redundant members of structures is perfectly general, subject to the limitations of using finite virtual displacements. An important feature is that it gives as many final equations of compatibility as there are redundants in the

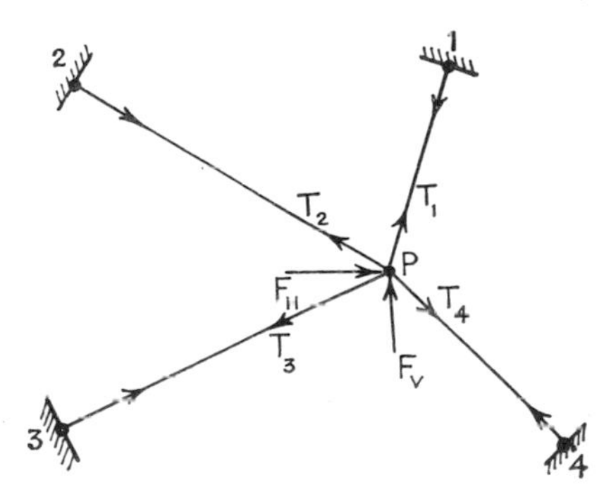

Fig. IV.10

system, in contrast with the method of strain energy or total potential energy which gives as many final equations (of equilibrium) as the number of geometrically independent components of deflection of joints, regardless of whether the system is redundant or not (see Chapter II, § 7; Chapter V, § 7; and Chapter VII, § 14). The method can be modified for use for structures whose members are subjected to bending as well as axial forces, and it is clearly not dependent upon particular load-deflection characteristics such as linear elasticity; linear characteristics are assumed above merely for the sake of simplicity of demonstration.

11. Method of taking account of " self-straining ".

In the event of a redundant structure being self-strained due to the redundant members having to be forced into place because of initial lack of fit, or again because of differential expansion effects, the compatibility equations can easily be modified to take account of these effects. Thus, if the two redundant members of the example of § 10 are initially too short by small amounts λ_3 and λ_4, respectively, for connection into the unloaded statically-determinate system, so that force has to be used to enable them to be connected, the compatibility conditions are

$$\begin{aligned} l_3 - e_3 &= (l_3 - \lambda_3) + a_3 T_3 \\ l_4 - e_4 &= (l_4 - \lambda_4) + a_4 T_4 \end{aligned} \qquad \text{(IV.38)}$$

or

$$\begin{aligned} e_3 + a_3 T_3 &= \lambda_3 \\ e_4 + a_4 T_4 &= \lambda_4 \end{aligned} \qquad \text{(IV.39)}$$

Provided that λ_3 and λ_4 are known, T_3 and T_4 can be found by these equations, because e_3 and e_4 are functions of T_3, T_4 and the loading as explained above.

12. The " reduction method " by virtual work.*

After finding the forces in the redundants, suppose it is necessary to find expressions for the deflections of joints. For this purpose it is possible to revert to the statically-determinate system loaded by the forces due to the redundant members as well as the applied loads, and consider the virtual work of suitable arbitrary systems of forces in equilibrium. In order to demonstrate the procedure in detail, it is sufficient to consider the

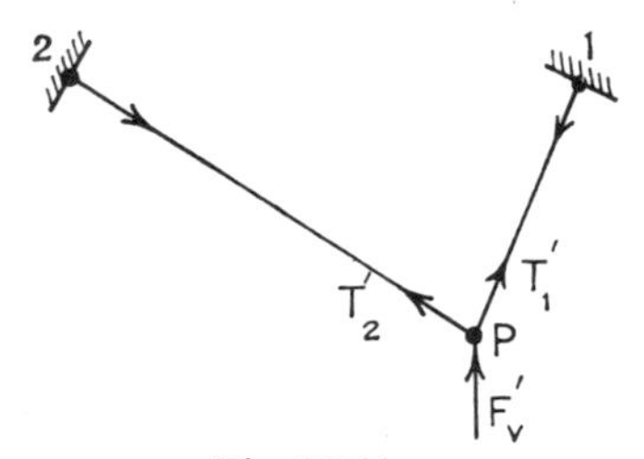

Fig. IV.11

structure with a single redundant member, as shown in fig. IV.7, so that the statically-determinate or reduced system is loaded as shown in fig. IV.8, and the expressions for the changes in length of the members of this system are in accordance with equations (IV.29). Thus, for v, the virtual work of the arbitrary system of forces in equilibrium, F'_V, T'_1, and T'_2, as shown in fig. IV.11, must be considered using virtual displacements equal to the actual deflections of the system, that is

$$F'_V v = T'_1 e_1 + T'_2 e_2 \qquad \text{(IV.40)}$$

* For application of this method to structures having members in bending see reference 27 of the Bibliography.

where

$$
\begin{aligned}
T_1' &= -F_V' \frac{\cos\alpha_2}{\sin\alpha_1 \cos\alpha_2 - \cos\alpha_1 \sin\alpha_2} \\
T_2' &= F_V' \frac{\cos\alpha_1}{\sin\alpha_1 \cos\alpha_2 - \cos\alpha_1 \sin\alpha_2}
\end{aligned} \tag{IV.41}
$$

and e_1 and e_2 are given by equations (IV.29). Therefore

$$
v = \frac{\begin{aligned} a_1[T_3(\cos\alpha_2 \sin\alpha_3 - \sin\alpha_2 \cos\alpha_3) + F_V \cos\alpha_2]\cos\alpha_2 \\ + a_2[T_3(\cos\alpha_1 \sin\alpha_3 - \sin\alpha_1 \cos\alpha_3) + F_V \cos\alpha_1]\cos\alpha_1 \end{aligned}}{(\sin\alpha_1 \cos\alpha_2 - \cos\alpha_1 \sin\alpha_2)^2} \tag{IV.42}
$$

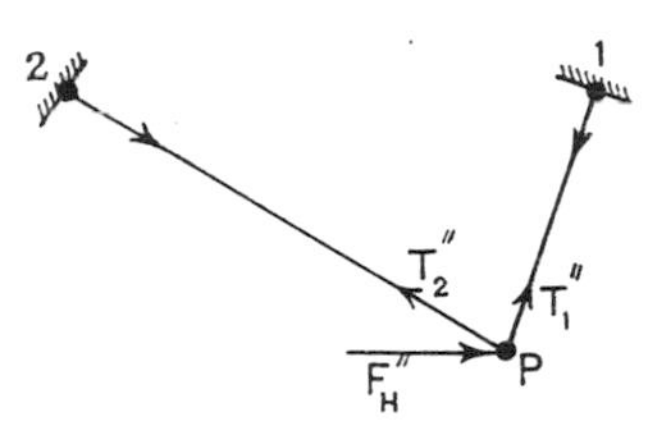

Fig. IV.12

Again, for h, the virtual work of the arbitrary system of forces in equilibrium, F_H'', T_2'', and T_1'', as shown in fig. IV.12, must be considered using the same system of virtual displacements, that is

$$
F_H'' h = T_1'' e_1 + T_2'' e_2 \tag{IV.43}
$$

where

$$
\begin{aligned}
T_1'' &= F_H'' \frac{\sin\alpha_2}{\sin\alpha_1 \cos\alpha_2 - \cos\alpha_1 \sin\alpha_2} \\
T_2'' &= -F_H'' \frac{\sin\alpha_1}{\sin\alpha_1 \cos\alpha_2 - \cos\alpha_1 \sin\alpha_2}
\end{aligned} \tag{IV.44}
$$

and as e_1 and e_2 are the same as before,

$$
h = \frac{\begin{aligned} -a_1[T_3(\cos\alpha_2 \sin\alpha_3 - \sin\alpha_2 \cos\alpha_3) + F_V \cos\alpha_2]\sin\alpha_2 \\ - a_2[T_3(\cos\alpha_1 \sin\alpha_3 - \sin\alpha_1 \cos\alpha_3) + F_V \cos\alpha_1]\sin\alpha_1 \end{aligned}}{(\sin\alpha_1 \cos\alpha_2 - \cos\alpha_1 \sin\alpha_2)^2} \tag{IV.45}
$$

This method, which is sometimes described as the "reduction method", of finding any deflection of a redundant system by using the reduced (statically-determinate) system and including the forces in the redundant members as determined by previous analysis with the loads, is very powerful and of general utility. It should be noted that the deflections so obtained are with reference to the unloaded configuration of the reduced system, which, for self-strained redundant systems, is not the same as the unloaded configuration of the redundant system (owing to the deformation of the reduced system due to the self-straining).

13. Virtual-work equation including forces in redundant members.

Although reduction to the statically-determinate system is useful for finding particular deflections as described, it is of course possible to write an equation of virtual work for a system to include the forces in the redundants. Thus, for the system shown in fig. IV.7, with the forces F_V, T_1, T_2, and T_3 in equilibrium, the equation of virtual work using virtual displacements equal to the deflections due to F_V is as follows:

$$F_V v = T_1 e_1 + T_2 e_2 + T_3 e_3 \tag{IV.46}$$

where e_1, e_2, and e_3 correspond to the senses of the forces T_1, T_2, and T_3, respectively: that is, if the members are in tension the values of e correspond to their lengthening and vice versa.

Therefore, after finding the forces in the redundant T_3 and then T_1 and T_2 and using the load-deflection characteristics for finding the changes in length e of the members, the deflection v can be found by equation (IV.46) as an alternative to equation (IV.40) in this particular example. If, however, there is a load F_H as well as F_V, the equation becomes

$$F_H h + F_V v = T_1 e_1 + T_2 e_2 + T_3 e_3 \tag{IV.47}$$

and neither h nor v can be found separately. In fact, the main value of such forms of virtual work lies in providing a means of verifying " conservation " of complementary energy, as mentioned in § 7 above, and equation (IV.20) applies whether the system is statically determinate or indeterminate.

Again, an arbitrary system of small compatible virtual displacements which satisfy the specified geometrical conditions can be used instead of h, v, e_1, e_2 and e_3, for example h', v', e'_1, e'_2 and e'_3; but the equation of virtual work of the type (IV.46) or (IV.47) is then only of academic interest in the present connection.

14. Example of advantageous application of the reduction method.

One of the more fascinating applications of the reduction method of finding the deflections individually is to multi-span redundant elastic structures. A simple example of this kind is shown in fig. IV.13. It is a two-span pin-jointed girder on rigid supports at A, B, and C, of which only A can provide horizontal restraint, and the spans are interconnected by a member EG. Without EG, each span would be statically determinate, and so this member will be treated as the redundant. If the vertical deflection at Q in span BC is required when a load F_{PV} is applied as shown

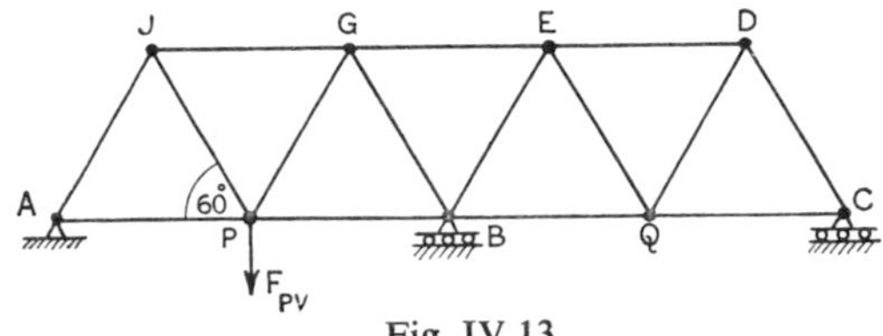

Fig. IV.13

at P in span AB, it is necessary to analyse the system first of all to find the forces in the members, and hence their changes in length. For this purpose, each span can be considered separately, loaded as shown in

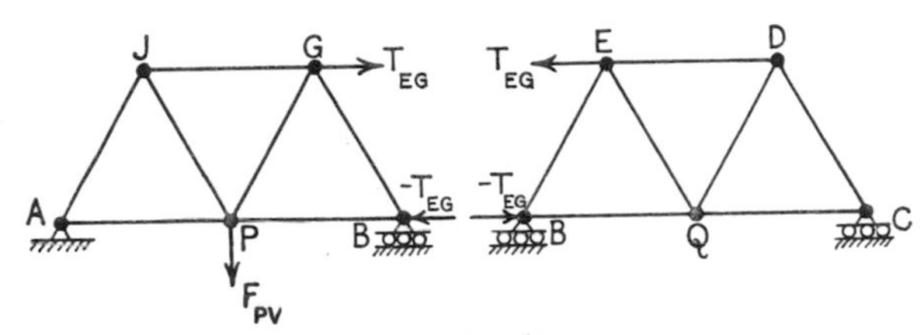

Fig. IV.14

fig. IV.14, and the forces T in the members found in terms of F_{PV} and T_{EG} by the conditions of equilibrium of the joints. These values are given in the second column of Table IV.1, where a positive sign denotes tension in a member. If all of the members have linear elasticity and the same flexibility a, their changes in length are simply $e = aT$ and are as shown in the third column of the table.

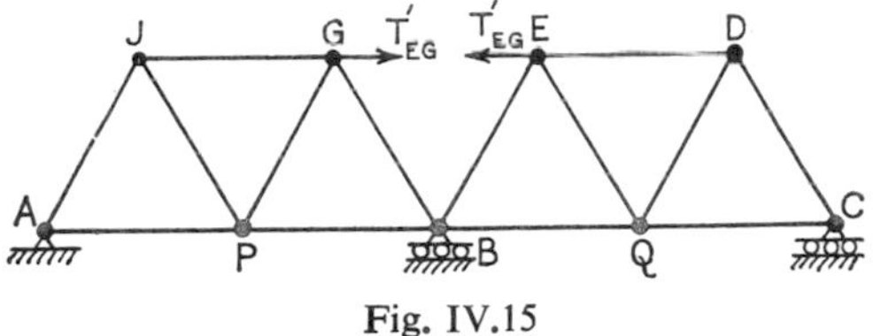

Fig. IV.15

Now to find T_{EG} in terms of F_{PV} it is necessary to consider the condition for the compatibility of the strains of the spans and the member EG. The change in the distance between E and G (e_{EG}) can be expressed in terms of F_{PV} and T_{EG} with the aid of the principle of virtual work, by considering the system of forces T' in equilibrium with arbitrary loads T'_{EG} shown in fig. IV.15. This system of forces is shown in the fourth column of the table. By the principle of virtual work using virtual displacements which are equal to the deflections produced by F_{PV}, the following equation is obtained:

$$T'_{EG}\, e_{EG} = \sum T'e \tag{IV.48}$$

TABLE IV.1

Member	Force T	Change in length $e = aT$	Force T'	$T'e$
AJ	$+\frac{1}{2}T_{EG} - \frac{1}{\sqrt{3}}F_{PV}$	$a(+\frac{1}{2}T_{EG} - \frac{1}{\sqrt{3}}F_{PV})$	$+\frac{1}{2}T'_{EG}$	$a(+\frac{1}{4}T_{EG} - \frac{1}{2\sqrt{3}}F_{PV})T'_{EG}$
AP	$-\frac{1}{4}T_{EG} + \frac{1}{2\sqrt{3}}F_{PV}$	$a(-\frac{1}{4}T_{EG} + \frac{1}{2\sqrt{3}}F_{PV})$	$-\frac{1}{4}T'_{EG}$	$a(+\frac{1}{16}T_{EG} - \frac{1}{8\sqrt{3}}F_{PV})T'_{EG}$
JP	$-\frac{1}{2}T_{EG} + \frac{1}{\sqrt{3}}F_{PV}$	$a(-\frac{1}{2}T_{EG} + \frac{1}{\sqrt{3}}F_{PV})$	$-\frac{1}{2}T'_{EG}$	$a(+\frac{1}{4}T_{EG} - \frac{1}{2\sqrt{3}}F_{PV})T'_{EG}$
GJ	$+\frac{1}{2}T_{EG} - \frac{1}{\sqrt{3}}F_{PV}$	$a(+\frac{1}{2}T_{EG} - \frac{1}{\sqrt{3}}F_{PV})$	$+\frac{1}{2}T'_{EG}$	$a(+\frac{1}{4}T_{EG} - \frac{1}{2\sqrt{3}}F_{PV})T'_{EG}$
GP	$+\frac{1}{2}T_{EG} + \frac{1}{\sqrt{3}}F_{PV}$	$a(+\frac{1}{2}T_{EG} + \frac{1}{\sqrt{3}}F_{PV})$	$+\frac{1}{2}T'_{EG}$	$a(+\frac{1}{4}T_{EG} + \frac{1}{2\sqrt{3}}F_{PV})T'_{EG}$
BP	$-\frac{3}{4}T_{EG} + \frac{1}{2\sqrt{3}}F_{PV}$	$a(-\frac{3}{4}T_{EG} + \frac{1}{2\sqrt{3}}F_{PV})$	$-\frac{3}{4}T'_{EG}$	$a(+\frac{9}{16}T_{EG} - \frac{3}{8\sqrt{3}}F_{PV})T'_{EG}$
BG	$-\frac{1}{2}T_{EG} - \frac{1}{\sqrt{3}}F_{PV}$	$-a(+\frac{1}{2}T_{EG} + \frac{1}{\sqrt{3}}F_{PV})$	$-\frac{1}{2}T'_{EG}$	$a(+\frac{1}{4}T_{EG} + \frac{1}{2\sqrt{3}}F_{PV})T'_{EG}$
BQ	$-\frac{3}{4}T_{EG}$	$-\frac{3}{4}aT_{EG}$	$-\frac{3}{4}T'_{EG}$	$+\frac{9}{16}aT_{EG}\,T'_{EG}$
BE	$-\frac{1}{2}T_{EG}$	$-\frac{1}{2}aT_{EG}$	$-\frac{1}{2}T'_{EG}$	$+\frac{1}{4}aT_{EG}\,T'_{EG}$
DE	$+\frac{1}{2}T_{EG}$	$+\frac{1}{2}aT_{EG}$	$+\frac{1}{2}T'_{EG}$	$+\frac{1}{4}aT_{EG}\,T'_{EG}$
EQ	$+\frac{1}{2}T_{EG}$	$+\frac{1}{2}aT_{EG}$	$+\frac{1}{2}T'_{EG}$	$+\frac{1}{4}aT_{EG}\,T'_{EG}$
DQ	$-\frac{1}{2}T_{EG}$	$-\frac{1}{2}aT_{EG}$	$-\frac{1}{2}T'_{EG}$	$+\frac{1}{4}aT_{EG}\,T'_{EG}$
CQ	$-\frac{1}{4}T_{EG}$	$-\frac{1}{4}aT_{EG}$	$-\frac{1}{4}T'_{EG}$	$+\frac{1}{16}aT_{EG}\,T'_{EG}$
CD	$+\frac{1}{2}T_{EG}$	$+\frac{1}{2}aT_{EG}$	$+\frac{1}{2}T'_{EG}$	$+\frac{1}{4}aT_{EG}\,T'_{EG}$

The quantities $T'e$ are as shown in the fifth column of the table and their algebraic sum is

$$\sum T'e = a\left(\frac{15}{4}T_{EG} - \frac{1}{\sqrt{3}}F_{PV}\right)T'_{EG} \qquad \text{(IV.49)}$$

therefore

$$e_{EG} = a\left(\frac{15}{4}T_{EG} - \frac{1}{\sqrt{3}}F_{PV}\right) \qquad \text{(IV.50)}$$

and the strained length EG is

$$l - e_{EG} = l - a\left(\frac{15}{4}T_{EG} - \frac{1}{\sqrt{3}}F_{PV}\right) \qquad \text{(IV.51)}$$

where l is the unstrained length of the members of the structure.

Considering now the member EG; if this member is subjected to a tensile force T_{EG} as assumed, its strained length is $l + aT_{EG}$. For compatibility of the strains of this member and the remainder of the structure, therefore,

$$l - a\left(\frac{15}{4}T_{EG} - \frac{1}{\sqrt{3}}F_{PV}\right) = l + a\,T_{EG}$$

so that

$$T_{EG} = +\frac{4}{19\sqrt{3}}F_{PV} \qquad \text{(IV.52)}$$

The final stage in the calculation of v_Q consists of considering the span BC alone loaded as shown in fig. IV.16. The changes in length of

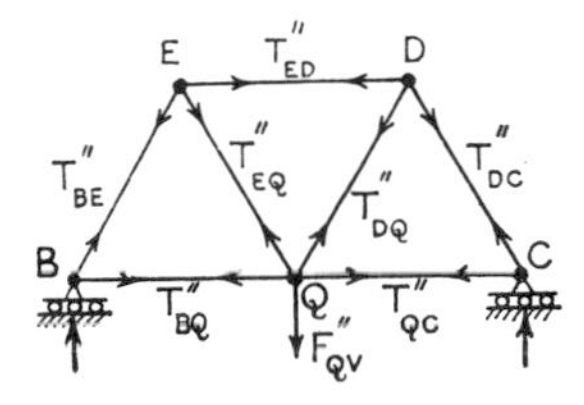

Fig. IV.16

the members are given in the second column of Table IV.2 and will be used as virtual displacements of the arbitrary system of member forces T'' in equilibrium with an arbitrary load F''_{QV}, as shown in fig. IV.16, so that

$$F''_{QV}\,v_Q = \sum T''e \qquad \text{(IV.53)}$$

The forces T'' are given in the third column of Table IV.2 and the products $T''e$ are given in the fourth column, from which

$$\sum T''e = -\frac{4a}{57}F_{PV}F''_{QV} \qquad \text{(IV.54)}$$

TABLE IV.2

Member	e	T''	$T''e$
BQ	$-\frac{3}{4}aT_{EG}$*	$+\frac{1}{2\sqrt{3}}F''_{QV}$	$-\frac{3}{38\times 3}aF_{PV}\,F''_{QV}$
BE	$-\frac{1}{2}aT_{EG}$	$-\frac{1}{\sqrt{3}}F''_{QV}$	$+\frac{2}{19\times 3}aF_{PV}\,F''_{QV}$
DE	$+\frac{1}{2}aT_{EG}$	$-\frac{1}{\sqrt{3}}F''_{QV}$	$-\frac{2}{19\times 3}aF_{PV}\,F''_{QV}$
EQ	$+\frac{1}{2}aT_{EG}$	$+\frac{1}{\sqrt{3}}F''_{QV}$	$+\frac{2}{19\times 3}aF_{PV}\,F''_{QV}$
DQ	$-\frac{1}{2}aT_{EG}$	$+\frac{1}{\sqrt{3}}F''_{QV}$	$-\frac{2}{19\times 3}aF_{PV}\,F''_{QV}$
CQ	$-\frac{1}{4}aT_{EG}$	$+\frac{1}{2\sqrt{3}}F''_{QV}$	$-\frac{1}{38\times 3}aF_{PV}\,F''_{QV}$
CD	$+\frac{1}{2}aT_{EG}$	$-\frac{1}{\sqrt{3}}F''_{QV}$	$-\frac{2}{19\times 3}aF_{PV}\,F''_{QV}$

* Where $T_{EG} = \frac{4}{19\sqrt{3}}F_{PV}$

Therefore, by equation (IV.53),

$$v_Q = -\frac{4a}{57}F_{PV} \qquad \text{(IV.55)}$$

where the minus sign signifies that v_Q is in the opposite sense to that of the arbitrary force F''_{QV}, i.e. v_Q is upwards, as would be expected having regard to the nature of the system.

15. Advantageous use of symmetry.

The force in the redundant EG in the previous example could have been found more readily owing to this particular structure being symmetrical and its characteristics being linear, by making use of symmetry and skew symmetry. Thus, the forces in the members could be found by superposing the results of the analyses for the symmetrical loading and the skew-symmetrical loading as shown in fig. IV.17. The force in EG is clearly zero in the latter instance, so that the forces in the members of the span BC due to the skew-symmetrical component of the loading can be found by statics. The symmetrical component of the loading is thus

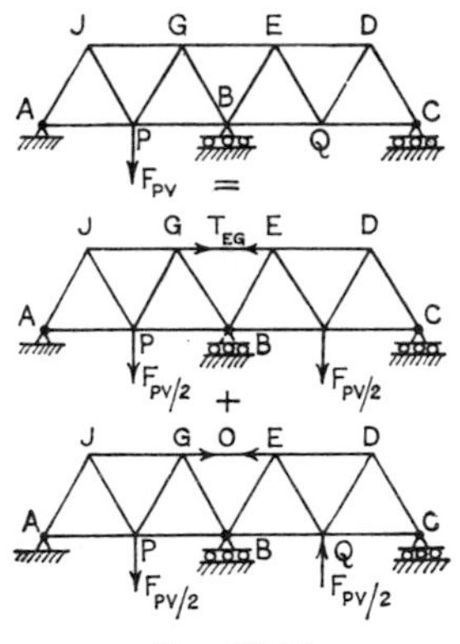

Fig. IV.17

the cause of the load in EG, and as this component of the loading causes identity of force distribution in the two spans, it is necessary to consider only one span, say AB, for the purpose of finding T_{EG} with the aid of virtual work in the manner described above.

16. Conclusion.

It is interesting that, although the principle of virtual work is basically a means of obtaining conditions of equilibrium, its main use in engineering science is in a modified form, as a means of finding deflections and conditions for the compatibility of strains of elastic systems such as metal structures.

V The Method of Complementary Energy

1. Introduction.

The complementary energy of an elastic system is defined in Chapter I as the integral of (deflection) $\times$ δ(load) and is represented graphically by the area above and to the left of the load-deflection curve as shown in fig. V.1. Its first derivative with respect to load or force gives the deflection of the system in the direction of the load at the point of application of the latter. Complementary energy is, therefore, useful for finding deflections of elastic systems and also for obtaining conditions for the compatibility of strains in connection with the analysis of redundant structures. It is an alternative to the principle of virtual work in these respects; in fact, the equations derived by both methods are identical. This is to be expected, however, because justification of the general method of complementary energy depends upon the principle of virtual work.

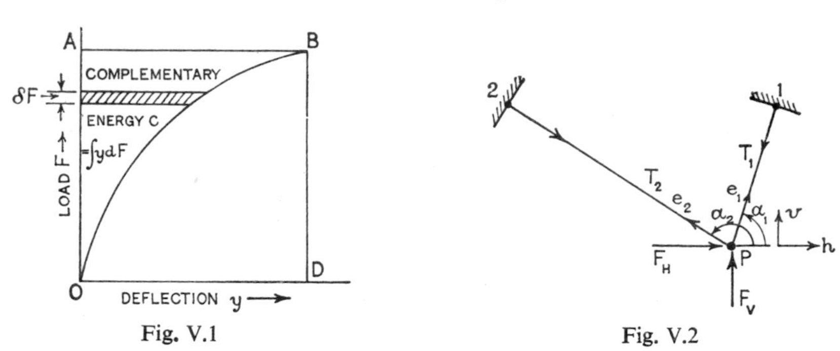

Fig. V.1

Fig. V.2

2. Properties of complementary energy.

A simple example is perhaps best for illustrating the salient features of complementary energy. If the pin-jointed elastic structure shown in fig. V.2 is loaded at P by forces F_V and F_H as shown, the complementary work of the loading C_L is

$$C_L = \int_0^{F_V} v\,dF_V + \int_0^{F_H} h\,dF_H \tag{V.1}$$

where v and h are the deflections of P in the lines of action of F_V and F_H respectively; and because F_V and F_H are independent,

$$\frac{\partial C_L}{\partial F_V} = v \qquad \frac{\partial C_L}{\partial F_H} = h \tag{V.2}$$

Advantage cannot be taken of this result as a method of finding deflections, however, because there is in general no convenient way of expressing v and h in terms of F_V and F_H respectively, but there is the complementary energy of the members C_M, as follows:

$$C_M = \int_0^{T_1} e_1\, dT_1 + \int_0^{T_2} e_2\, dT_2 \tag{V.3}$$

where e_1 and e_2 are the changes in length of the members which are associated with the forces T_1 and T_2 respectively. The member forces T_1 and T_2 depend upon F_V and F_H and, so long as e_1 and e_2 are not large enough to cause a significant change in the geometry of the structure, it is an easy matter to express T_1 and T_2 in terms of F_V and F_H by the conditions of equilibrium of P. Also, by means of the load-deflection characteristics of the members, e_1 and e_2 can be expressed in terms of T_1 and T_2 respectively, and hence in terms of F_V and F_H. If, therefore, $C_M = C_L$,

$$\begin{aligned} \frac{\partial C_M}{\partial F_V} &= \frac{\partial C_L}{\partial F_V} = v \\ \frac{\partial C_M}{\partial F_H} &= \frac{\partial C_L}{\partial F_H} = h \end{aligned} \tag{V.4}$$

so that expressions v and h could be found without difficulty. In fact, $C_M = C_L$ as a consequence of the principle of virtual work when virtual displacements equal to the deflections actually produced by F_V and F_H can be used, as described in Chapter IV, § 7; that is, when the deflections produced by the loads are not so large as to cause the geometry of the loaded structure to be significantly different from that of the unloaded structure. By the principle of virtual work using virtual displacements equal to actual displacements or deflections, therefore,

$$F_V v + F_H h = T_1 e_1 + T_2 e_2 \tag{V.5}$$

The significance of this equation is shown graphically in fig. V.3 and, if arbitrary load-deflection curves are included as shown, it is evident that

$$\int_0^{F_V} v\, dF_V + \int_0^{F_H} h\, dF_H = \int_0^{T_1} e_1\, dT_1 + \int_0^{T_2} e_2\, dT_2 \tag{V.6}$$

or

$$C_L = C_M = C$$

because by the law of conservation of energy

$$\int_0^v F_V\,dv + \int_0^h F_H\,dh = \int_0^{e_1} T_1\,de_1 + \int_0^{e_2} T_2\,de_2 \tag{V.7}$$

and equation (V.5) expresses the result of combining equations (V.6) and (V.7).

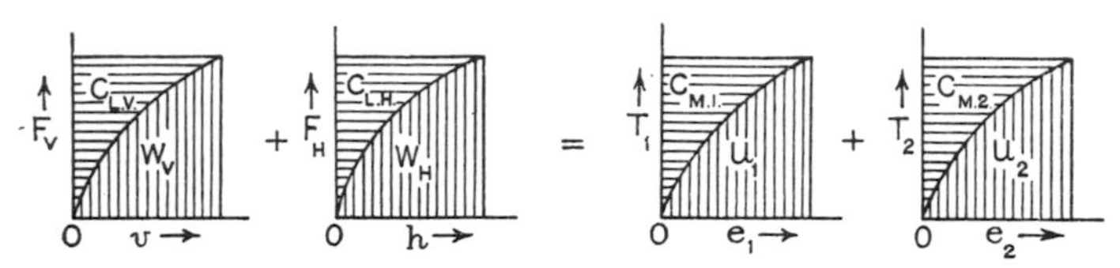

Fig. V.3

As the majority of engineering structures are designed so that their form is not conducive to large deflections when they are loaded, " conservation of complementary energy " is usually valid and is independent of the load-deflection characteristics of the individual members of a structure.

3. Use of complementary energy for finding deflections.

It is appropriate now to consider the details of the method of complementary energy for obtaining expressions for the deflections v and h of the simple system shown in fig. V.2. For this purpose it is convenient to assume that the members have linear load-deflection characteristics such that $e_1 = a_1 T_1$ and $e_2 = a_2 T_2$, where e_1 and e_2 are small enough to have a negligible effect upon the geometry of the system. By the principle of conservation of complementary energy

$$\delta C = v\,\delta F_V + h\,\delta F_H = e_1\,\delta T_1 + e_2\,\delta T_2 \tag{V.8}$$

so that

$$\begin{aligned} \frac{\partial C}{\partial F_V} &= v = e_1 \frac{\partial T_1}{\partial F_V} + e_2 \frac{\partial T_2}{\partial F_V} \\ \frac{\partial C}{\partial F_H} &= h = e_1 \frac{\partial T_1}{\partial F_H} + e_2 \frac{\partial T_2}{\partial F_H} \end{aligned} \tag{V.9}$$

By the conditions of equilibrium of P, assuming that the members are in tension,

$$\begin{aligned} T_1 \sin\alpha_1 + T_2 \sin\alpha_2 + F_V &= 0 \\ T_1 \cos\alpha_1 + T_2 \cos\alpha_2 + F_H &= 0 \end{aligned} \tag{V.10}$$

Therefore

$$T_1 = -\frac{F_V \cos\alpha_2 - F_H \sin\alpha_2}{\sin\alpha_1 \cos\alpha_2 - \cos\alpha_1 \sin\alpha_2}$$
$$T_2 = \frac{F_V \cos\alpha_1 - F_H \sin\alpha_1}{\sin\alpha_1 \cos\alpha_2 - \cos\alpha_1 \sin\alpha_2} \tag{V.11}$$

so that

$$\frac{\partial T_1}{\partial F_V} = -\frac{\cos\alpha_2}{\sin\alpha_1 \cos\alpha_2 - \cos\alpha_1 \sin\alpha_2}; \quad \frac{\partial T_1}{\partial F_H} = \frac{\sin\alpha_2}{\sin\alpha_1 \cos\alpha_2 - \cos\alpha_1 \sin\alpha_2}$$
$$\frac{\partial T_2}{\partial F_V} = \frac{\cos\alpha_1}{\sin\alpha_1 \cos\alpha_2 - \cos\alpha_1 \sin\alpha_2}; \quad \frac{\partial T_2}{\partial F_H} = -\frac{\sin\alpha_1}{\sin\alpha_1 \cos\alpha_2 - \cos\alpha_1 \sin\alpha_2} \tag{V.12}$$

Substituting in equations (V.9) and taking into account that $e_1 = a_1 T_1$ and $e_2 = a_2 T_2$,

$$\frac{\partial C}{\partial F_V} = v = \frac{a_1(F_V \cos\alpha_2 - F_H \sin\alpha_2)\cos\alpha_2 + a_2(F_V \cos\alpha_1 - F_H \sin\alpha_1)\cos\alpha_1}{(\sin\alpha_1 \cos\alpha_2 - \cos\alpha_1 \sin\alpha_2)^2}$$
$$\frac{\partial C}{\partial F_H} = h = \frac{-a_1(F_V \cos\alpha_2 - F_H \sin\alpha_2)\sin\alpha_2 - a_2(F_V \cos\alpha_1 - F_H \sin\alpha_1)\sin\alpha_1}{(\sin\alpha_1 \cos\alpha_2 - \cos\alpha_1 \sin\alpha_2)^2} \tag{V.13}$$

or, combining coefficients of F_V and F_H,

$$\frac{\partial C}{\partial F_V} = v = \frac{(a_1 \cos^2\alpha_2 + a_2 \cos^2\alpha_1)F_V - (a_1 \sin\alpha_2 \cos\alpha_2 + a_2 \sin\alpha_1 \cos\alpha_1)F_H}{(\sin\alpha_1 \cos\alpha_2 - \cos\alpha_1 \sin\alpha_2)^2}$$
$$\frac{\partial C}{\partial F_H} = h = \frac{-(a_1 \sin\alpha_2 \cos\alpha_2 + a_2 \sin\alpha_1 \cos\alpha_1)F_V + (a_1 \sin\alpha_2^2 + a_2 \sin^2\alpha_1)F_H}{(\sin\alpha_1 \cos\alpha_2 - \cos\alpha_1 \sin\alpha_2)^2} \tag{V.14}$$

It is emphasized that all of the steps in the use of the complementary energy as above are essentially independent of whether or not the members of the system have linear or non-linear characteristics.

4. Reciprocal properties of coefficients of forces (linear systems only).

It is again interesting to note (see also Chapter II, § 6) that equations (V.14) clearly exhibit the reciprocal property of linear elastic systems. The coefficients of F_V and F_H in these equations are flexibility coefficients of the structure, that is, the equations can be rewritten

$$v = a_{VV} F_V + a_{VH} F_H$$
$$h = a_{HV} F_V + a_{HH} F_H \tag{V.15}$$

where $a_{VH} = a_{HV}$ in accordance with the reciprocal theorem. The precise physical significance of the flexibility coefficients a are considered in

Chapter VII, § 3. The form of equations (V.15) is the inversion of that of equations (II.20) in which the concept of stiffness is used. The behaviour of linear systems can always be expressed either in terms of coefficients of flexibility or in terms of coefficients of stiffness.

5. Fictitious-load method of finding deflections by complementary energy.

In the event of either F_V or F_H being zero it is merely necessary to rewrite equations (V.14) accordingly; this gives a clue for obtaining the deflection of a system by the complementary-energy method in a direction in which there is no force or load. By considering a fictitious load F_Q to be applied at the appropriate point in the direction in which the deflection (q) is required, in addition to the actual loads, the quantity $q\,\delta F_Q$ is introduced in the expression for the variation of the complementary energy. This enables $\partial C/\partial F_Q = q$ to be found, and the required value of q is obtained by putting $F_Q = 0$.

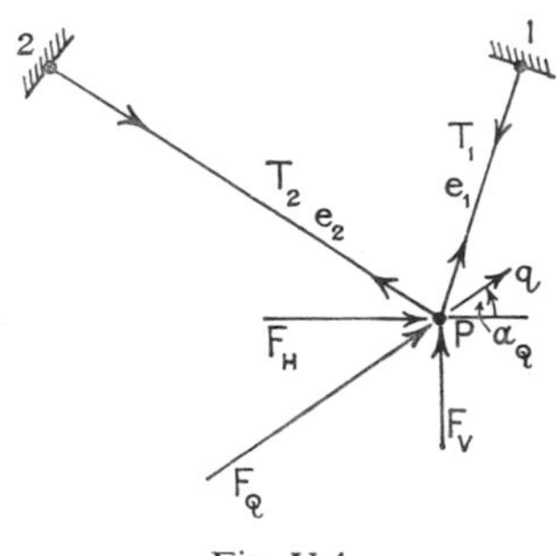

Fig. V.4

Thus to find the deflection (q) of P (fig. V.4) in any direction due to the loads F_V and F_H by the complementary-energy method, consider a fictitious load F_Q acting in the appropriate direction:

$$\delta C = v\,\delta F_V + h\,\delta F_H + q\,\delta F_Q = e_1\,\delta T_1 + e_2\,\delta T_2 \tag{V.16}$$

whence

$$\left(\frac{\partial C}{\partial F_Q}\right)_{F_Q=0} = q = \left(e_1\frac{\partial T_1}{\partial F_Q} + e_2\frac{\partial T_2}{\partial F_Q}\right)_{F_Q=0} \tag{V.17}$$

Now, by the conditions of equilibrium of P,

$$T_1 = -\frac{(F_V + F_Q\sin\alpha_Q)\cos\alpha_2 - (F_H + F_Q\cos\alpha_Q)\sin\alpha_2}{\sin\alpha_1\cos\alpha_2 - \cos\alpha_1\sin\alpha_2}$$

$$T_2 = \frac{(F_V + F_Q\sin\alpha_Q)\cos\alpha_1 - (F_H + F_Q\cos\alpha_Q)\sin\alpha_1}{\sin\alpha_1\cos\alpha_2 - \cos\alpha_1\sin\alpha_2} \tag{V.18}$$

therefore

$$\frac{\partial T_1}{\partial F_Q} = -\frac{\sin\alpha_Q\cos\alpha_2 - \cos\alpha_Q\sin\alpha_2}{\sin\alpha_1\cos\alpha_2 - \cos\alpha_1\sin\alpha_2}$$

$$\frac{\partial T_2}{\partial F_Q} = +\frac{\sin\alpha_Q\cos\alpha_1 - \cos\alpha_Q\sin\alpha_1}{\sin\alpha_1\cos\alpha_2 - \cos\alpha_1\sin\alpha_2} \tag{V.19}$$

and if $e_1 = a_1T_1$ and $e_2 = a_2T_2$, substitution in equation (V.17) having regard to equations (V.18) and putting $F_Q = 0$ gives the deflection q due to F_V and F_H, as follows:

$$q = \frac{\begin{array}{l}[a_1(F_V \cos\alpha_2 - F_H \sin\alpha_2)\cos\alpha_2 + a_2(F_V\cos\alpha_1 - F_H\sin\alpha_1)\cos\alpha_1]\sin\alpha_Q \\ \quad + [a_1(F_V\cos\alpha_2 - F_H\sin\alpha_2)\sin\alpha_2 + a_2(F_V\cos\alpha_1 - F_H\sin\alpha_1)\sin\alpha_1]\cos\alpha_Q\end{array}}{(\sin\alpha_1\cos\alpha_2 - \cos\alpha_1\sin\alpha_2)^2} \qquad \text{(V.20)}$$

In this instance, it is clear from geometrical considerations that

$$q = v\sin\alpha_Q + h\cos\alpha_Q \qquad \text{(V.21)}$$

and equation (V.20) is merely this equation including the expressions for v and h as given by equations (V.13). Equations (V.13) are, of course, appropriate since $F_Q = 0$.

6. Identity of variation of complementary energy with virtual work.

Equations such as (V.8) and (V.16), which express conservation of complementary energy following an infinitesimally small change in the loading of an elastic system, can also be regarded as equations of virtual work. Equation (V.8), for example, is as follows:

$$v\,\delta F_V + h\,\delta F_H = e_1\,\delta T_1 + e_2\,\delta T_2$$

where v, h, e_1, and e_2 are a system of displacements which are compatible with the geometry of the structure and, moreover, represent deflections which are actually produced by loads F_V and F_H applied to the system shown in fig. V.2. Also δF_V and δF_H are in equilibrium with δT_1 and δT_2. Equation (V.8) is, therefore, the equation of the virtual work of the system of forces in equilibrium, δF_V, δF_H, δT_1, and δT_2, as the result of a virtual displacement described by the compatible system represented by v, h, e_1, and e_2, being the deflections actually associated with the system of forces F_V, F_H, T_1, and T_2. Equation (V.16) can be treated similarly.

7. Analysis of statically-indeterminate systems with the aid of complementary energy.

The method of complementary energy is useful for obtaining the equations for the compatibility of strains within statically-indeterminate (redundant) elastic structures once the conditions of equilibrium of forces have been applied. These equations, which are as numerous as the redundants, are sufficient to enable the forces in the redundants to be found. This method of analysing redundant systems is the same in principle as that using virtual work described in Chapter IV, § 9 and 10, and the remarks there about its features are relevant. The approach is the alternative to that involved in either the method of strain energy or the method of potential energy.

For the purpose of illustrating the complementary-energy method for redundant systems the analysis of the pin-jointed structure with one redundant member shown in fig. V.5 is suitable. Once again, for the sake of avoiding complication which contributes nothing to the principles involved, the members of the structure are assumed to have linear elasticity. The equation of the variation of complementary energy, assuming that the deflections v and h do not alter the geometry of the system significantly, is as follows:

$$\delta C = v\,\delta F_V + h\,\delta F_H = e_1\,\delta T_1 + e_2\,\delta T_2 + e_3\,\delta T_3 \qquad (V.22)$$

where the symbols have the same meaning as before, respectively, and the subscript 3 refers to the additional member (redundant). Now as there are only two independent equations of equilibrium of the joint P, the force in the redundant must be treated as an independent variable with respect to equilibrium, like the loads F_V and F_H, since by these equations it is possible to eliminate only two variables, i.e. T_1 and T_2 (or T_1 and T_3, if the member 2 is treated as redundant). Thus, by equation (V.22),

$$\begin{aligned} \frac{\partial C}{\partial T_3} &= 0 = e_1 \frac{\partial T_1}{\partial T_3} + e_2 \frac{\partial T_2}{\partial T_3} + e_3 \\ \frac{\partial C}{\partial F_V} &= v = e_1 \frac{\partial T_1}{\partial F_V} + e_2 \frac{\partial T_2}{\partial F_V} \\ \frac{\partial C}{\partial F_H} &= h = e_1 \frac{\partial T_1}{\partial F_H} + e_2 \frac{\partial T_2}{\partial F_H} \end{aligned} \qquad (V.23)$$

where the first equation represents the condition for the compatibility of the strain of the redundant member with that of the statically-determinate system consisting of members 1 and 2, and is the means whereby T_3 can be found, having eliminated T_1 and T_2 by means of the equations of equilibrium:

$$\begin{aligned} T_1 \sin\alpha_1 + T_2 \sin\alpha_2 + T_3 \sin\alpha_3 + F_V &= 0 \\ T_1 \cos\alpha_1 + T_2 \cos\alpha_2 + T_3 \cos\alpha_3 + F_H &= 0 \end{aligned} \qquad (V.24)$$

Thus

$$\begin{aligned} T_1 &= -\frac{(F_V \cos\alpha_2 - F_H \sin\alpha_2) + T_3(\cos\alpha_2 \sin\alpha_3 - \sin\alpha_2 \cos\alpha_3)}{\sin\alpha_1 \cos\alpha_2 - \cos\alpha_1 \sin\alpha_2} \\ T_2 &= \frac{(F_V \cos\alpha_1 - F_H \sin\alpha_1) + T_3(\cos\alpha_1 \sin\alpha_3 - \sin\alpha_1 \cos\alpha_3)}{\sin\alpha_1 \cos\alpha_2 - \cos\alpha_1 \sin\alpha_2} \end{aligned} \qquad (V.25)$$

Substitution in the first of equations (V.23), taking into account that $e_1 = a_1 T_1$, $e_2 = a_2 T_2$, and $e_3 = a_3 T_3$, gives

$$\frac{\partial C}{\partial T_3} = 0 = \frac{\begin{array}{l} a_1(\cos\alpha_2 \sin\alpha_3 - \sin\alpha_2 \cos\alpha_3)\,[(F_V \cos\alpha_2 - F_H \sin\alpha_2) + T_3(\cos\alpha_2 \sin\alpha_3 \\ -\sin\alpha_2\cos\alpha_3)] + a_2(\cos\alpha_1 \sin\alpha_3 - \sin\alpha_1\cos\alpha_3)\,[(F_V\cos\alpha_1 - F_H\sin\alpha_1) \\ + T_3(\cos\alpha_1\sin\alpha_3 - \sin\alpha_1\cos\alpha_3)] \end{array}}{(\sin\alpha_1\cos\alpha_2 - \cos\alpha_1\sin\alpha_2)^2} + a_3 T_3 \qquad \text{(V.26)}$$

This equation is sufficient to enable T_3 to be expressed in terms of the loads F_V and F_H and is identical to equation (IV.36) if $F_H = 0$. After finding T_3 in this way, T_1 and T_2 can be found by means of equations (V.25) and then the deflections v and h by the second and third of equations (V.23).

8. Generalization of the method of complementary energy for analysing statically-indeterminate systems.

The procedure adopted in § 7 could be followed for the analysis of a system with any number r of redundant members. The equations of internal compatibility would be r in number:

$$\frac{\partial C}{\partial T_i} = 0 \quad (i = 1, 2, \ldots, r) \qquad \text{(V.27)}$$

and would be sufficient to enable the forces T_i $(i = 1, 2, \ldots, r)$ in the redundants to be found. Equation (V.27) can be interpreted as specifying that among the systems of internal forces of an elastic structure which are in equilibrium with the impressed forces or loads, the actual one is such that it renders the complementary energy stationary.

9. Interpretation of stationary complementary energy—self-straining.

The stationary property can be interpreted by considering the application of the complementary-energy method to a system which is self-strained in the sense that stresses are present before loads are applied, due to either initial lack of fit of redundant members or differential expansion as a result of temperature variation. Suppose the redundant member of the system shown in fig. V.5 is initially too short by a small amount λ, and that external forces T_3 as shown in fig. V.6 are applied in order to enable the member to be connected, at the same time as the loads F_V and F_H are applied.* Variation of the complementary energy is, therefore,

$$\delta C = v\,\delta F_V + h\,\delta F_H + \lambda\,\delta T_3 = e_1\,\delta T_1 + e_2\,\delta T_2 + e_3\,\delta T_3 \qquad \text{(V.28)}$$

* Consideration of self-straining due to temperature variation enables an alternative concept to be used for application of the complementary-energy method to this kind of problem as described in Chapter VI, §§ 2 and 3.

because the external force T_3 does work through a distance λ while F_V and F_H do work through v and h respectively. The forces T_1 and T_2 are given by equations (V.25) and the changes in length of the members are $e_1 = a_1T_1$, $e_2 = a_2T_2$, $e_3 = a_3T_3$. This means that the only difference between equations (V.22) and (V.28) is in respect of the term $\lambda\,\delta T_3$ which is added to the left-hand side, so that

$$\frac{\partial C}{\partial T_3} = \lambda = \frac{\begin{array}{l} a_1(\cos\alpha_2\sin\alpha_3 - \sin\alpha_2\cos\alpha_3)\,[(F_V\cos\alpha_2 - F_H\sin\alpha_2) + T_3(\cos\alpha_2\sin\alpha_3 \\ -\sin\alpha_2\cos\alpha_3)] + a_2(\cos\alpha_1\sin\alpha_3 - \sin\alpha_1\cos\alpha_3)\,[(F_V\cos\alpha_1 - F_H\sin\alpha_1) \\ +\,T_3(\cos\alpha_1\sin\alpha_3 - \sin\alpha_1\cos\alpha_3)] \end{array}}{(\sin\alpha_1\cos\alpha_2 - \cos\alpha_1\sin\alpha_2)^2} + a_3T_3 \tag{V.29}$$

Also

$$\frac{\partial C}{\partial F_V} = v \quad \text{and} \quad \frac{\partial C}{\partial F_H} = h \tag{V.30}$$

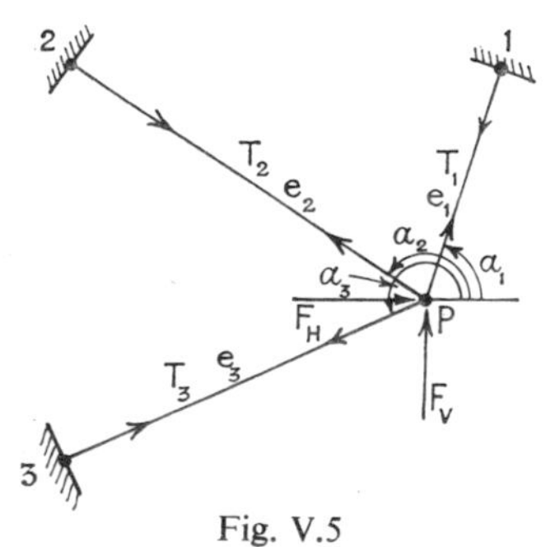

Fig. V.5

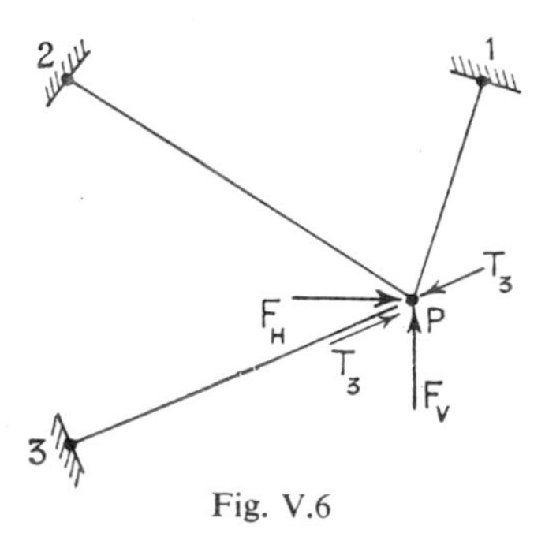

Fig. V.6

where v and h are deflections with reference to the position of the joint P when $F_V = F_H = T_3 = 0$, i.e. the position of P when the redundant member is cut out. In order to find the actual deflections v' and h' of the self-strained redundant system, it is necessary in general to put $F_V = F_H = 0$ in equations (V.30) first of all to obtain v_0 and h_0, then

$$v' = v - v_0 \quad \text{and} \quad h' = h - h_0 \tag{V.31}$$

In general when there are r redundant members in a structure, each of which initially lacks fit by being small amounts λ_i $(i = 1, 2, \ldots, r)$ too short, variation of the complementary energy gives

$$\frac{\partial C}{\partial T_i} = \lambda_i \quad (i = 1, 2, \ldots, r) \tag{V.32}$$

because

$$\delta C = \sum v\,\delta F_V + \sum h\,\delta F_H + \sum_1^r \lambda_i\,\delta T_i$$

The complementary energy of a system is, then, stationary with respect to the forces in the redundant members only when self-straining is absent.

10. Use of strain energy instead of complementary energy for linear systems.

When the system consists entirely of members with linear elasticity the complementary energy and the strain energy are identical if gross distortion is absent (see Chapter I, § 3) so that equation (V.27) can be written

$$\frac{\partial U}{\partial T_i} = 0 \qquad (i = 1, 2, \ldots, r) \tag{V.33}$$

and represents Castigliano's principle of least work. Again, equation (V.32) becomes

$$\frac{\partial U}{\partial T_i} = \lambda_i \qquad (i = 1, 2, \ldots, r) \tag{V.34}$$

Southwell has suggested* that the term " least work " signifies that the strain energy of a system which is not self-strained is always less than that of a self-strained system. A similar statement cannot be made in general concerning complementary energy, because it is not possible to state that the complementary energy of a non-linear elastic system is greater as a result of self-straining. The reason for this is that, while the complementary energy or the strain energy of a linear elastic system is always positive, since it consists entirely of terms of squares of the variables and is therefore positive definite, the complementary energy of a non-linear system depends upon the sign of the variables. In any case, no useful purpose is served by determining whether the property of stationary complementary energy represents a maximum or a minimum. Indeed, it is unfortunate that Castigliano's principle, represented by equation (V.33), was ever identified with the concept of least work and the implication of natural economy, because it is a peculiarity of linear systems and is not applicable to conservative systems generally.

11. Alternative derivation of the complementary-energy method of analysis.

It is interesting to consider the derivation of equation (V.32) on the lines which Castigliano used for the derivation of equation (V.34). By imagining all of the redundant members to be replaced by an equivalent system of loads T_i $(i = 1, 2, \ldots, r)$ applied to the statically-determinate system, as well as the actual loads $F_{V1}, F_{V2}, \ldots ; F_{H1}, F_{H2}, \ldots$, etc., the deflection e_1 of the statically-determinate system in the line of any redundant member can be expressed as

$$\frac{\partial C_s}{\partial T_i} = e_i \qquad (i = 1, 2, \ldots, r) \tag{V.35}$$

* Reference 11 of the Bibliography.

where C_s represents the complementary energy of the statically-determinate system. Therefore, if the loads T_i represent tension of the ith redundant member, the distance l_i of the statically-determinate system in the line of the ith redundant member is $l_i - e_i$ after loading. But the ith redundant member is, in fact, loaded in tension by T_i and its unstrained length is $l_i - \lambda_i$ while its change of length due to T_i is

$$\frac{dC_{mi}}{dT_i} = e_i' \tag{V.36}$$

where C_{mi} is the complementary energy of this member, so that its strained length is $l_i - \lambda_i + e_i'$. Since this member is actually accommodated in the structure within the distance $l_i - e_i$, however,

$$l_i - e_i = l_i - \lambda_i + e_i' \tag{V.37}$$

or

$$-e_i = -\lambda_i + e_i'$$

Therefore

$$-\frac{\partial C_s}{\partial T_i} = -\lambda_i + \frac{dC_{mi}}{dT_i}$$

or

$$\frac{\partial}{\partial T_i}(C_s + C_{mi}) = \lambda_i \tag{V.38}$$

Because the complementary energies of the individual redundant members are independent, equation (V.38) can be written alternatively as

$$\frac{\partial}{\partial T_i}\left(C_s + \sum_1^r C_{mi}\right) = \lambda_i. \qquad (i = 1, 2, \ldots, r) \tag{V.39}$$

and putting $C_s + \sum C_{mi} = C$, the complementary energy of the statically-indeterminate or redundant system,

$$\frac{\partial C}{\partial T_i} = \lambda_i \qquad (i = 1, 2, \ldots, r) \qquad \text{(equation V.32)}$$

When there is no self-straining λ_i $(i = 1, 2, \ldots, r) = 0$ so that

$$\frac{\partial C}{\partial T_i} = 0 \qquad (i = 1, 2, \ldots, r) \qquad \text{(equation V.27)}$$

12. Limitations on the use of complementary energy.

In order to illustrate the kind of circumstances in which the complementary-energy method is invalid, suppose a load F_V is applied to the pin-jointed elastic system shown in fig. V.7. Clearly, in order that the system can withstand a vertical load it is necessary for it to assume a configuration such as that shown in chain-dotted lines, so that the forces in the members have a component in the direction of the load. The conditions of equilibrium of P are, therefore, as follows:

$$\begin{aligned} -T_1 \sin \alpha_1' - T_2 \sin \alpha_2' + F_V &= 0 \\ +T_1 \cos \alpha_1' - T_2 \cos \alpha_2' &= 0 \end{aligned} \tag{V.40}$$

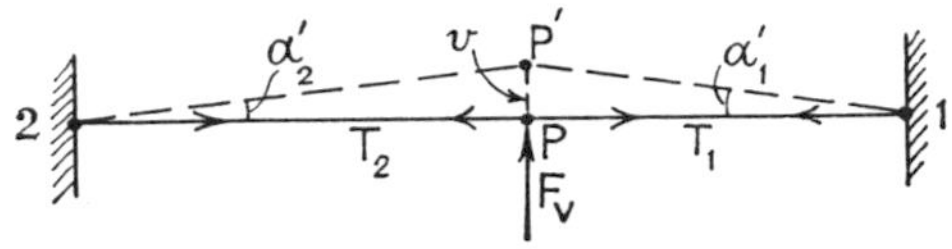

Fig. V.7

and the changes of length of the members are such that

$$\begin{aligned} \sin \alpha_1' &= \frac{v}{l_1 + e_1} = \frac{\sqrt{(2e_1 l_1 + e_1^2)}}{l_1 + e_1}; \quad \cos \alpha_1' = \frac{l_1}{l_1 + e_1} \\ \sin \alpha_2' &= \frac{v}{l_2 + e_2} = \frac{\sqrt{(2e_2 l_2 + e_2^2)}}{l_2 + e_2}; \quad \cos \alpha_2' = \frac{l_2}{l_2 + e_2} \end{aligned} \tag{V.41}$$

Equations (V.40) and (V.41) are sufficient, with the aid of the load-deflection characteristics of the members, to enable T_1 and T_2 to be found. It is clear that even if the members have linear elasticity, the form of the relationship between F_V and v will be non-linear. The sum of the strain

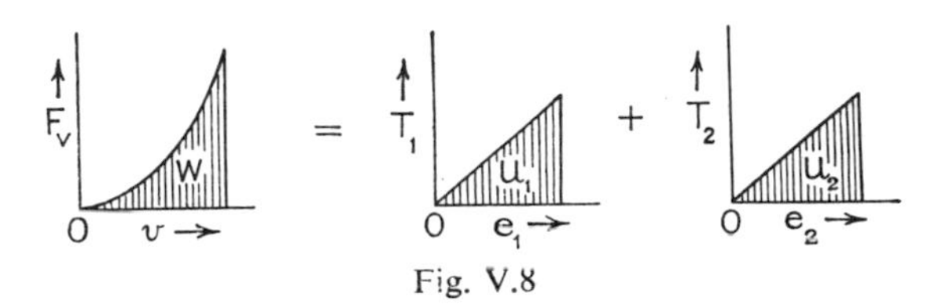

Fig. V.8

energies of the members is equal to the work done by F_V, by the law of conservation of energy, as shown pictorially in fig. V.8. But because the system of displacements e_1, e_2, and v are not compatible with the geometry of the loaded system (or with that of the unloaded system), they are unsuitable as virtual displacements of P, and so the complementary "work done" by F_V is not equal to the sum of the complementary energies of the members; that is, while

$$F_V \, \delta v = T_1 \, \delta e_1 + T_2 \, \delta e_2 \tag{V.42}$$

$$F_V \, v \neq T_1 \, e_1 + T_2 \, e_2 \tag{V.43}$$

and

$$\delta C = v \, \delta F_V \neq e_1 \, \delta T_1 + e_2 \, \delta T_2 \tag{V.44}$$

Although it is still true that $dC/dF_V = v$, as C cannot be computed without finding v in the process, the relationship is valueless. Thus, while it is always possible to express the deflection of an elastic system at a load point in this way, only when complementary energy is conserved is the expression of any value.

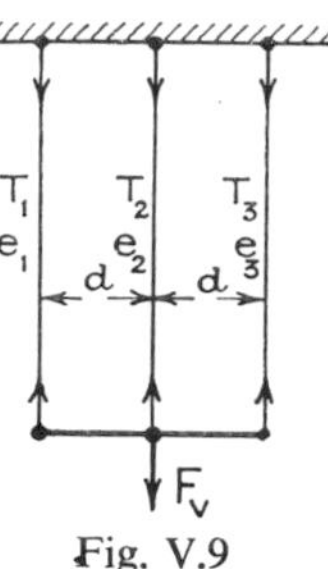

Fig. V.9

13. Example of the use of complementary energy for the analysis of a non-linear system.

Application of the method of complementary energy in the analysis of the hypothetical non-linear elastic system with one redundant member shown in fig. V.9 affords comparison of this approach (which, as stated in § 7 above, is similar to that demonstrated in Chapter IV, § 9) with that demonstrated with reference to the same problem in Chapter II, § 11. Variation of the complementary energy is as follows:

$$\delta C = e_2\,\delta F_V = e_1\,\delta T_1 + e_2\,\delta T_2 + e_3\,\delta T_3 \qquad \text{(V.45)}$$

The forces in the members T_1, T_2, and T_3 and the load F_V are related by the two conditions of equilibrium

$$\begin{aligned} T_1 + T_2 + T_3 - F_V &= 0 \\ T_1 - T_3 &= 0 \end{aligned} \qquad \text{(V.46)}$$

Choosing the member with the force T_1 as the redundant,

because
$$\begin{aligned} T_2 &= F_V - 2T_1 \\ T_3 &= T_1 \end{aligned} \qquad \text{(V.47)}$$

Also, the load-deflection characteristics of the members are such that

$$\begin{aligned} e_1 &= a_1 T_1{}^2 \\ e_2 &= a_2 T_2 = a_2(F_V - 2T_1) \\ e_3 &= a_3 T_3 = a_3 T_1 \end{aligned} \qquad \text{(V.48)}$$

Substituting from equations (V.47) and (V.48) in equation (V.45) gives

$$\delta C = e_2\,\delta F_V = a_1\,T_1^2\,\delta T_1 + a_2(F_V - 2T_1)(\delta F_V - 2\delta T_1) + a_3\,T_1\,\delta T_1 \qquad \text{(V.49)}$$

$$\begin{aligned} \frac{\partial C}{\partial T_1} &= 0 = a_1 T_1^2 - 2a_2(F_V - 2T_1) + a_3 T_1 \\ \frac{\partial C}{\partial F_V} &= e_2 = a_2(F_V - 2T_1) \end{aligned} \qquad \text{(V.50)}$$

By the former of these equations

$$T_1 = -\frac{1}{2a_1}[(4a_2+a_3)\pm\sqrt{\{(4a_2+a_3)^2+8a_1 a_2 F_V\}}] = T_3 \qquad \text{(V.51)}$$

which is the same as the second of equations (II.31). It is now possible to write the expression for T_2 and also that for e_2 in terms of F_V and the coefficients a_1, a_2 and a_3. The remarks in Chapter II, § 11 and Chapter III, § 5 concerning the correct physical interpretation of the results of analysing some non-linear systems apply in this instance also.

14. Changing of variables or coordinates.

In making use of the complementary-energy method there is complete freedom in respect of choice of working variables or coordinates (see also Chapter II, § 12); that is, instead of working in terms of forces explicitly, any more convenient system of variables which represents the forces or combinations of them can be used, so long as the conditions of equilibrium are satisfied in terms of such variables. The obvious alternative to the explicit use of forces is the use of deflections to represent the forces in the process of analysis. Thus, in the previous example it is possible to write

$$\begin{aligned} T_1 &= \frac{1}{a_1^{\frac{1}{2}}} e_1^{\frac{1}{2}} = b_1 e_1^{\frac{1}{2}} \\ T_2 &= \frac{1}{a_2} e_2 = b_2 e_2 \\ T_3 &= \frac{1}{a_3} e_3 = b_3 e_3 \end{aligned} \qquad \text{(V.52)}$$

By applying the conditions of equilibrium (V.46) e_2 and e_3 can be expressed in terms of e_1 as follows:

$$\begin{aligned} e_3 &= \frac{b_1}{b_3} e_1^{\frac{1}{2}} \\ e_2 &= \frac{1}{b_2}(F_V - 2b_1 e_1^{\frac{1}{2}}) \end{aligned} \qquad \text{(V.53)}$$

Variation of the complementary energy in terms of deflections as variables is, therefore,

$$\delta C = e_2\,\delta F_V = \tfrac{1}{2} b_1\, e_1^{\frac{1}{2}}\,\delta e_1 + b_2\, e_2\,\delta e_2 + b_3\, e_3\,\delta e_3 \qquad \text{(V.54)}$$

and substituting from equations (V.53) gives

$$\delta C = e_2\,\delta F_V = \tfrac{1}{2}b_1\,e_1^{\frac{1}{2}}\,\delta e_1 + \frac{1}{b_2}(F_V - 2b_1\,e_1^{\frac{1}{2}})(\delta F_V - b_1\,e_1^{-\frac{1}{2}}\,\delta e_1) + \frac{b_1^2}{2b_3}\,\delta e_1$$

whence

$$\begin{aligned} \frac{\partial C}{\partial e_1} &= 0 = \tfrac{1}{2}b_1 e_1^{\frac{1}{2}} - \frac{b_1}{b_2}(F_V e_1^{-\frac{1}{2}} - 2b_1) + \frac{b_1^2}{2b_3} \\ \frac{\partial C}{\partial F_V} &= e_2 = \frac{1}{b_2}(F_V - 2b_1\,e_1^{\frac{1}{2}}) \end{aligned} \qquad \text{(V.55)}$$

Thus, by the first of equations (V.55), putting $a_1 = 1/b_1^2$, $a_2 = 1/b_2$ and $a_3 = 1/b_3$,

$$e_1 = \frac{1}{4a_1}[-(4a_2 + a_3) + \sqrt{\{(4a_2 + a_3)^2 + 8a_1\,a_2\,F_V\}}]^2 \qquad \text{(V.56)}$$

so that now e_2 and e_3 can be found. In order to find the forces T_1, T_2, and T_3 it is merely necessary to make use of equations (V.52).

15. Conclusions.

Additional examples of the application of the method of complementary energy are given in Chapter VI. It is clear that in the capacity in which complementary energy is used in the illustrative examples of this Chapter it is merely a means of deriving final equations for compatibility or deflections, a process which can be performed without using the energy concept, even though it might then be more tedious. A powerful method of obtaining approximate solutions is, however, afforded by the use of complementary energy (Chapter VIII).

VI Further Examples of the Use of the Complementary-Energy Method

1. Introduction.

In Chapter III examples of the use of the potential- and strain-energy methods are given. For the purpose of comparing the approach underlying those methods with that of the complementary-energy method, the same examples are considered in this chapter with reference to the complementary-energy method.

2. Example 1. Self-strained system.

Particulars of the pin-jointed elastic system ABDG with one redundant and loads F_{BV}, F_{BH}, F_{DV}, and F_{DH}, shown in fig. VI.1, are given in Chapter III, § 2. The members of the system have linear elasticity: the stiffness of AB, BD, and DG is b, while that of BG and AD is $b/\sqrt{2}$. In addition to the strains caused by the loading, there is expansion of the members due to a rise in temperature. If AB, BD, and DG were free to expand, the length of each would increase by λ; similarly, the length of BG would increase by $2\sqrt{2}\lambda$, and that of AD would increase by $\sqrt{2}\lambda$.

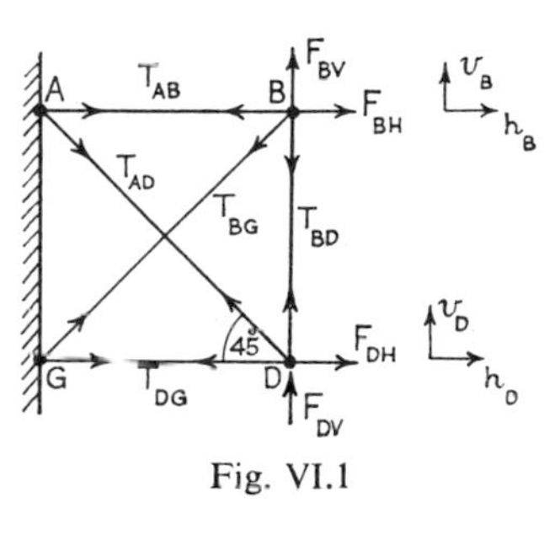

Fig. VI.1

The equation of the conservation of complementary energy for a small variation of the system of forces is

$$\begin{aligned}\delta C &= v_B\,\delta F_{BV}+h_B\,\delta F_{BH}+v_D\,\delta F_{DV}+h_D\,\delta F_{DH} \\ &= e_{AB}\,\delta T_{AB}+e_{BD}\,\delta T_{BD}+e_{DG}\,\delta T_{DG}+e_{AD}\,\delta T_{AD}+e_{BG}\,\delta T_{BG}\end{aligned} \qquad \text{(VI.1)}$$

It should be noted that this is also the equation of virtual work of the forces δT_{AB}, δT_{BD}, . . . ; δF_{BV}, δF_{BH}; δF_{DV}, δF_{DH} in equilibrium when compatible virtual displacements equal to the displacements which actually occur when the system is strained are considered.

If BD is chosen as the redundant member, then the forces in the other members (the statically-determinate system) depends upon T_{BD} as well as F_{BV}, F_{BH}, F_{DV}, and F_{DH} for equilibrium. Thus, the following equation of compatibility of the redundant member and the statically-determinate system can be obtained from equation (VI.1):

$$\frac{\partial C}{\partial T_{BD}} = e_{AB}\frac{\partial T_{AB}}{\partial T_{BD}} + e_{BD} + e_{DG}\frac{\partial T_{DG}}{\partial T_{BD}} + e_{AD}\frac{\partial T_{AD}}{\partial T_{BD}} + e_{BG}\frac{\partial T_{BG}}{\partial T_{BD}} = 0 \quad \text{(VI.2)}$$

Similarly, the following equations of the deflections of the joints B and D are obtained:

$$\begin{aligned} \frac{\partial C}{\partial F_{BV}} &= e_{AB}\frac{\partial T_{AB}}{\partial F_{BV}} + e_{BD}\,.\,0 + e_{DG}\frac{\partial T_{DG}}{\partial F_{BV}} + e_{AD}\frac{\partial T_{AD}}{\partial F_{BV}} + e_{BG}\frac{\partial T_{BG}}{\partial F_{BV}} = v_B \\ \frac{\partial C}{\partial F_{BH}} &= e_{AB}\frac{\partial T_{AB}}{\partial F_{BH}} + e_{BD}\,.\,0 + e_{DG}\frac{\partial T_{DG}}{\partial F_{BH}} + e_{AD}\frac{\partial T_{AD}}{\partial F_{BH}} + e_{BG}\frac{\partial T_{BG}}{\partial F_{BH}} = h_B \\ \frac{\partial C}{\partial F_{DV}} &= e_{AB}\frac{\partial T_{AB}}{\partial F_{DV}} + e_{BD}\,.\,0 + e_{DG}\frac{\partial T_{DG}}{\partial F_{DV}} + e_{AD}\frac{\partial T_{AD}}{\partial F_{DV}} + e_{BG}\frac{\partial T_{BG}}{\partial F_{DV}} = v_D \\ \frac{\partial C}{\partial F_{DH}} &= e_{AB}\frac{\partial T_{AB}}{\partial F_{DH}} + e_{BD}\,.\,0 + e_{DG}\frac{\partial T_{DG}}{\partial F_{DH}} + e_{AD}\frac{\partial T_{AD}}{\partial F_{DH}} + e_{BG}\frac{\partial T_{BG}}{\partial F_{DH}} = h_D \end{aligned} \quad \text{(VI.3)}$$

Now the conditions of equilibrium of the joints B and D are

$$\begin{aligned} T_{BD} + \frac{1}{\sqrt{2}}T_{BG} &= F_{BV} \\ T_{AB} + \frac{1}{\sqrt{2}}T_{BG} &= F_{BH} \\ T_{BD} + \frac{1}{\sqrt{2}}T_{AD} &= -F_{DV} \\ T_{DG} + \frac{1}{\sqrt{2}}T_{AD} &= F_{DH} \end{aligned} \quad \text{(VI.4)}$$

therefore

$$\begin{aligned} T_{AB} &= F_{BH} - F_{BV} + T_{BD} \\ T_{DG} &= F_{DH} + F_{DV} + T_{BD} \\ T_{AD} &= -\sqrt{2}(F_{DV} + T_{BD}) \\ T_{BG} &= \sqrt{2}(F_{BV} - T_{BD}) \end{aligned} \quad \text{(VI.5)}$$

Also the changes in length of the members in terms of forces and temperature effects are as follows:

$$e_{AB} = \frac{1}{b} T_{AB} + \lambda = \frac{1}{b}(F_{BH} - F_{BV} + T_{BD}) + \lambda$$

$$e_{DG} = \frac{1}{b} T_{DG} + \lambda = \frac{1}{b}(F_{DH} + F_{DV} + T_{BD}) + \lambda$$

$$e_{AD} = \frac{\sqrt{2}}{b} T_{AD} + \sqrt{2}\lambda = -\frac{2}{b}(F_{DV} + T_{BD}) + \sqrt{2}\lambda \qquad \text{(VI.6)}$$

$$e_{BG} = \frac{\sqrt{2}}{b} T_{BG} + 2\sqrt{2}\lambda = \frac{2}{b}(F_{BV} - T_{BD}) + 2\sqrt{2}\lambda$$

$$e_{BD} = \frac{1}{b} T_{BD} + \lambda$$

Substitution from equation (VI.6) in equations (VI.2) and (VI.3) and using equations (VI.5) to obtain the partial derivatives of the forces in the statically-determinate system with respect to the loads and the force in the redundant gives

$$\frac{\partial C}{\partial T_{BD}} = \frac{1}{b}(3+4\sqrt{2})T_{BD} - \frac{1}{b}(1+2\sqrt{2})F_{BV} + \frac{1}{b}F_{BH} + \frac{1}{b}(1+2\sqrt{2})F_{DV} + \frac{1}{b}F_{DH} - 3\lambda = 0 \qquad \text{(VI.7)}$$

$$\frac{\partial C}{\partial F_{BV}} = -\frac{1}{b}(1+2\sqrt{2})T_{BD} + \frac{1}{b}(1+2\sqrt{2})F_{BV} - \frac{1}{b}F_{BH} + 0 + 0 + 3\lambda = v_B$$

$$\frac{\partial C}{\partial F_{BH}} = \frac{1}{b}T_{BD} - \frac{1}{b}F_{BV} + \frac{1}{b}F_{BH} + 0 + 0 + \lambda = h_B$$

$$\text{(VI.8)}$$

$$\frac{\partial C}{\partial F_{DV}} = \frac{1}{b}(1+2\sqrt{2})T_{BD} + 0 + 0 + \frac{1}{b}(1+2\sqrt{2})F_{DV} + \frac{1}{b}F_{DH} - \lambda = v_D$$

$$\frac{\partial C}{\partial F_{DH}} = \frac{1}{b}T_{BD} + 0 + 0 + \frac{1}{b}F_{DV} + \frac{1}{b}F_{DH} + \lambda = h_D$$

By equation (VI.7)

$$T_{BD} = 0{\cdot}44\,F_{BV} - 0{\cdot}12\,F_{BH} - 0{\cdot}44\,F_{DV} - 0{\cdot}12\,F_{DH} + 0{\cdot}34\,b\lambda \qquad \text{(VI.9)}$$

and when $F_{BV} = F_{BH} = F_{DH} = 0$

$$T_{BD} = -0{\cdot}44\,F_{DV} + 0{\cdot}34\,b\lambda \qquad \text{(VI.10)}$$

Upon substituting for T_{BD} from equation (VI.10) in equations (VI.8), the following values of the deflections of the joints B and D when $F_{BV} = F_{BH} = F_{DH} = 0$ are obtained:

$$\begin{aligned} v_B &= \frac{1\cdot69}{b}F_{DV}+1\cdot70\lambda \\ h_B &= -\frac{0\cdot44}{b}F_{DV}+1\cdot34\lambda \\ v_D &= \frac{2\cdot14}{b}F_{DV}+0\cdot30\lambda \\ h_D &= \frac{0\cdot56}{b}F_{DV}+1\cdot34\lambda \end{aligned} \qquad \text{(VI.11)}$$

The amount of the deflections which are caused by the loading is found simply by putting $\lambda = 0$, since v_B, h_B, v_D, and h_D are measured from the position of the joints of the unloaded system when there is no self-straining and the system is linear.

The results of this analysis agree with those of Chapter III, § 2. In order to find the forces in the members of the statically-determinate system in terms of the loads it is merely necessary to substitute the expression for T_{BD} from equation (VI.9) or (VI.10) in equations (VI.5). It is interesting to note that whereas by the strain-energy method it is necessary to solve four simultaneous equations of equilibrium before any of the unknowns can be found, as there is only one redundant BD, it is possible here to find T_{BD} immediately from the single compatibility equation (VI.7).

3. Discussion of treatment of self-straining by the complementary-energy method.

The method of using complementary energy for deriving the compatibility and deflection equations for a self-strained system demonstrated above is somewhat different from that described in Chapter V, § 9. By the latter, the self-straining is introduced in terms of lack of fit of the redundant members, whereas by the alternative procedure above, the effect is embraced in writing the changes of length of each member as in equations (VI.6). To clarify this, suppose that instead of temperature effects member BD, as the redundant, is initially too short by an amount λ, so that force has to be used to connect it between B and D. By this alternative procedure equations (VI.1) to (VI.5) are written as above and equations (VI.6) are modified as follows:

$$e_{AB} = \frac{1}{b} T_{AB} = \frac{1}{b}(F_{BH} - F_{BV} + T_{BD})$$

$$e_{DG} = \frac{1}{b} T_{DG} = \frac{1}{b}(F_{DH} + F_{DV} + T_{BD})$$

$$e_{AD} = \frac{\sqrt{2}}{b} T_{AD} = -\frac{2}{b}(F_{DV} + T_{BD}) \qquad \text{(VI.12)}$$

$$e_{BG} = \frac{\sqrt{2}}{b} T_{BG} = \frac{2}{b}(F_{BV} - T_{BD})$$

$$e_{BD} = \frac{1}{b} T_{BD} - \lambda$$

Thus the initial shortness of BD is treated as though it is caused by a differential temperature effect on the complete system. By using these equations in equation (VI.2) and proceeding on the lines set out in § 2, then:

$$\frac{\partial C}{\partial T_{BD}} = 0 \qquad \text{(VI.13)}$$

where

$$C = \int_0^{T_{AB}} e_{AB}\, dT_{AB} + \int_0^{T_{DG}} e_{DG}\, dT_{DG} + \int_0^{T_{AD}} e_{AD}\, dT_{AD} + \int_0^{T_{BG}} e_{BG}\, dT_{BG} + \int_0^{T_{BD}} e_{BD}\, dT_{BD} \qquad \text{(VI.14)}$$

but equally

$$\frac{\partial C}{\partial T_{BD}} = \lambda \qquad \text{(VI.15)}$$

when

$$C = \int_0^{T_{AB}} e_{AB}\, dT_{AB} + \int_0^{T_{DG}} e_{DG}\, dT_{DG} + \int_0^{T_{AD}} e_{AD}\, dT_{AD} + \int_0^{T_{BG}} e_{BG}\, dT_{BG} + \int_0^{T_{BD}} e'_{BD}\, dT_{BD} \qquad \text{(VI.16)}$$

if $e'_{BD} = \frac{1}{b} T_{BD}$, which is in accordance with the results of Chapter V, § 9.

Justification of this alternative method of applying complementary energy to self-strained systems depends upon regarding the equation of the variation of complementary energy such as (VI.1) as primarily an equation of virtual work. It should be noted that the alternative complementary-energy expressions of equations (VI.14) and (VI.16) differ in respect of the contribution of member BD only (the cause of self-straining). The

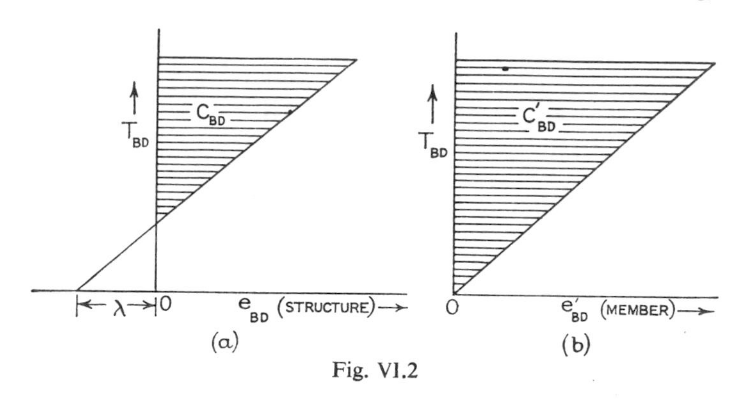

Fig. VI.2

significance of this difference is shown graphically in fig. VI.2. It really amounts to treating e_{BD} as a displacement in the system as distinct from e'_{BD}, the change in length of the redundant due to T_{BD}.

4. Example 2. Non-linear system.

The hypothetical plane pin-jointed system ABDG shown in fig. VI.3 is described in Chapter III, § 4. The joints A and G are fixed, joints B

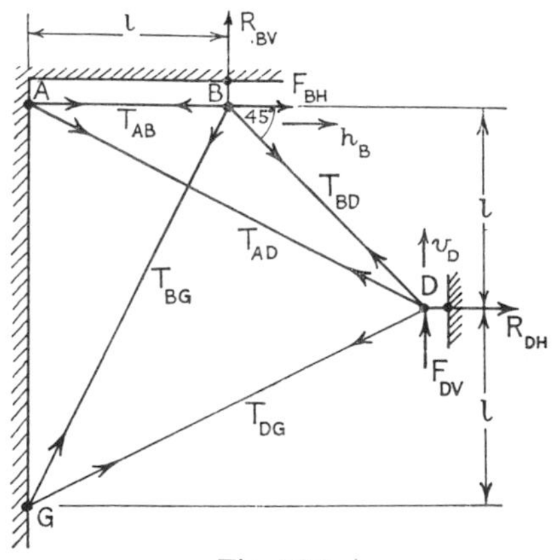

Fig. VI.3

can deflect horizontally only, and joint D can deflect vertically only. Consequently there are three redundants, say, member BD and the reactions R_{BV} and R_{DH} at B and D respectively shown in fig. VI.3. The stiffness of the linearly elastic member AB is b and that of other members except BD is $b/\sqrt{5}$. The load-deflection characteristic of BD is non-linear as shown in fig. III.3. The system is loaded by forces F_{BH} and F_{DV} as shown.

In order to analyse the loaded system by setting up the equations of compatibility of the strains of the redundants and the statically-determinate system, the complementary-energy method is used as follows:

$$\begin{aligned}\delta C &= h_B \delta F_{BH} + v_D \delta F_{DV} \\ &= e_{AB}\delta T_{AB} + e_{BD}\delta T_{BD} + e_{AD}\delta T_{AD} + e_{BG}\delta T_{BG} + e_{DG}\delta T_{DG}\end{aligned} \quad \text{(VI.17)}$$

from which the necessary three conditions of compatibility are

$$\begin{aligned}\frac{\partial C}{\partial T_{BD}} &= e_{AB}\frac{\partial T_{AB}}{\partial T_{BD}} + e_{BD} + e_{AD}\frac{\partial T_{AD}}{\partial T_{BD}} + e_{BG}\frac{\partial T_{BG}}{\partial T_{BD}} + e_{DG}\frac{\partial T_{DG}}{\partial T_{BD}} = 0 \\ \frac{\partial C}{\partial R_{BV}} &= e_{AB}\frac{\partial T_{AB}}{\partial R_{BV}} + 0 \quad + e_{AD}\frac{\partial T_{AD}}{\partial R_{BV}} + e_{BG}\frac{\partial T_{BG}}{\partial R_{BV}} + e_{DG}\frac{\partial T_{DG}}{\partial R_{BV}} = 0 \quad \text{(VI.18)} \\ \frac{\partial C}{\partial R_{DH}} &= e_{AB}\frac{\partial T_{AB}}{\partial R_{DH}} + 0 \quad + e_{AD}\frac{\partial T_{AD}}{\partial R_{DH}} + e_{BG}\frac{\partial T_{BG}}{\partial R_{DH}} + e_{DG}\frac{\partial T_{DG}}{\partial R_{DH}} = 0\end{aligned}$$

the forces in the redundants being independent with respect to the conditions of equilibrium of the system. In addition the equations for the deflections of the joints B and D are

$$\begin{aligned}\frac{\partial C}{\partial F_{BH}} &= e_{AB}\frac{\partial T_{AB}}{\partial F_{BH}} + 0 + e_{AD}\frac{\partial T_{AD}}{\partial F_{BH}} + e_{BG}\frac{\partial T_{BG}}{\partial F_{BH}} + e_{DG}\frac{\partial T_{DG}}{\partial F_{BH}} = h_B \\ \frac{\partial C}{\partial F_{DV}} &= e_{AB}\frac{\partial T_{AB}}{\partial F_{DV}} + 0 + e_{AD}\frac{\partial T_{AD}}{\partial F_{DV}} + e_{BG}\frac{\partial T_{BG}}{\partial F_{DV}} + e_{DG}\frac{\partial T_{DG}}{\partial F_{DV}} = v_D\end{aligned} \quad \text{(VI.19)}$$

Now the conditions of equilibrium assuming that tensile forces in members are positive are

$$\begin{aligned}T_{AB} + \frac{1}{\sqrt{5}}T_{BG} - \frac{1}{\sqrt{2}}T_{BD} &= F_{BH} \\ \frac{2}{\sqrt{5}}T_{BG} + \frac{1}{\sqrt{2}}T_{BD} &= R_{BV} \\ \frac{1}{\sqrt{5}}T_{AD} - \frac{1}{\sqrt{5}}T_{DG} + \frac{1}{\sqrt{2}}T_{BD} &= -F_{DV} \\ \frac{2}{\sqrt{5}}T_{AD} + \frac{2}{\sqrt{5}}T_{DG} + \frac{1}{\sqrt{2}}T_{BD} &= R_{DH}\end{aligned} \quad \text{(VI.20)}$$

therefore

$$
\begin{aligned}
T_{AB} &= F_{BH}-\frac{1}{2}R_{BV}+\frac{3}{2\sqrt{2}}T_{BD} \\
T_{AD} &= -\frac{\sqrt{5}}{2}F_{DV}+\frac{\sqrt{5}}{4}R_{DH}-\frac{3}{4}\sqrt{\frac{5}{2}}T_{BD} \\
T_{BG} &= \frac{\sqrt{5}}{2}R_{BV}-\frac{1}{2}\sqrt{\frac{5}{2}}T_{BD} \\
T_{DG} &= \frac{\sqrt{5}}{2}F_{DV}+\frac{\sqrt{5}}{4}R_{DH}+\frac{1}{4}\sqrt{\frac{5}{2}}T_{BD}
\end{aligned}
\qquad \text{(VI.21)}
$$

and, making use of the load-deflection characteristics of the members,

$$
\begin{aligned}
e_{AB} &= \frac{1}{b}T_{AB} = \frac{1}{b}\left(F_{BH}-\frac{1}{2}R_{BV}+\frac{3}{2\sqrt{2}}T_{BD}\right) \\
e_{BD} &= \frac{\sqrt{2}}{b}(2T_{BD}\pm k) \\
e_{AD} &= \frac{\sqrt{5}}{b}T_{AD} = -\frac{5}{2b}\left(F_{DV}-\frac{1}{2}R_{DH}+\frac{3}{2\sqrt{2}}T_{BD}\right) \\
e_{BG} &= \frac{\sqrt{5}}{b}T_{BG} = \frac{5}{2b}\left(R_{BV}-\frac{1}{\sqrt{2}}T_{BD}\right) \\
e_{DG} &= \frac{\sqrt{5}}{b}T_{DG} = \frac{5}{2b}\left(F_{DV}+\frac{1}{2}R_{DH}+\frac{1}{2\sqrt{2}}T_{BD}\right)
\end{aligned}
\qquad \text{(VI.22)}
$$

Substitution from equations (VI.21) and (VI.22) in equations (VI.18) gives, after simplification, the following three simultaneous equations of compatibility in terms of the forces in the three redundants:

$$
\begin{aligned}
20{\cdot}00\,T_{BD}-5{\cdot}68\,R_{BV}-2{\cdot}24\,R_{DH}\pm 3{\cdot}20k+2{\cdot}40\,F_{BH}+8{\cdot}94\,F_{DV} &= 0 \\
-10{\cdot}00\,T_{BD}+12{\cdot}20\,R_{BV}+0+0-2{\cdot}00\,F_{BH}+0 &= 0 \\
-15{\cdot}80\,T_{BD}+0+22{\cdot}40\,R_{DH}+0+0+0 &= 0
\end{aligned}
\qquad \text{(VI.23)}
$$

If $F_{DV} = 10k$ and $F_{BH} = 0$, then assuming that the redundant BD is in compression and $T_{BD} > k$ numerically, so that the sign of $3{\cdot}20k$ in the first of equations (VI.23) is negative, the equations give

$$T_{BD} = -6{\cdot}75k \quad : \quad R_{BV} = -5{\cdot}56k \quad : \quad R_{DH} = -4{\cdot}77k \qquad \text{(VI.24)}$$

This solution is in agreement with that obtained with the aid of the potential-energy method in Chapter III, § 4. Mainly because the number of redundants is greater than the number of components of deflection, the method of analysis demonstrated here is more laborious than the alternative by the potential-energy method. Thus, it is necessary to set up and solve three simultaneous equations of compatibility for the redundants, whereas by the equilibrium approach there are only two simultaneous equations of equilibrium to be set up and solved for the deflections. Moreover, the additional labour of substituting from equations (VI.21), (VI.22), and (VI.24) in equations (VI.19) to obtain the deflections h_B and v_D is appreciable, whereas by the alternative method it is relatively easy, having obtained the deflections, to find the force in any member.

The remarks in Chapter III, § 5, concerning the general difficulties of analysing non-linear systems apply equally to the method of analysis demonstrated above.

VII Some Properties of Systems with Linear Characteristics

1. Introduction.

In Chapters I and V attention was called to the property of elastic systems which obey Hooke's law and are said to be linear, whereby the strain energy can be identified with the complementary energy for purposes of deriving expressions for deflections and conditions of compatibility of strains. The best-known property of linear systems is, however, that of superposition, whereby the effect of, say, a system of applied forces is the same as the sum of the effects of the individual forces applied separately. This property enables applied forces or loads to be expressed in terms of constant coefficients of stiffness and the deflections, as noted in Chapter II, § 6. Alternatively, it enables deflections to be expressed in terms of constant coefficients of flexibility and the loads as noted in Chapter V, § 4. This Chapter is mainly concerned with considering in some detail the concepts of stiffness and flexibility of linear systems and their properties. The value of these concepts lies mainly in their affording systematization in the setting up of equations in the analysis of linear statically-indeterminate systems. They are, in fact, frequently a useful alternative to energy methods, when the approximate procedures derived from the latter are not appropriate.

Since the properties of stiffness and flexibility of linear systems are closely related to the reciprocal theorem, for which Maxwell, Betti, and Rayleigh are all given credit, and which is of considerable importance, this theorem is also considered in some detail in this Chapter.

2. Flexibility and stiffness.

The simplest linear elastic system is the linear spring. The deflection y of such a spring due to a force F applied to it is

$$y = aF \qquad \text{(VII.1)}$$

where a is the flexibility of the spring, being the deflection caused by unit force, and is constant since this equation expresses the linear relationship between the deflection and load on the spring.

Alternatively, the force applied to the spring can be expressed as

$$F = \frac{1}{a} y = by \tag{VII.2}$$

where $1/a = b$ is the stiffness of the spring, being the force required to cause unit deflection. Although in this simple example with only one degree of freedom the stiffness coefficient is the reciprocal of the flexibility coefficient, when there is more than one degree of freedom the individual stiffness coefficients are not merely the reciprocals of the respective flexibility coefficients. Rather is the stiffness of a system as a whole the reciprocal or inversion of the flexibility of the system. In order to consider the flexibility and the stiffness of a system as a whole, matrix notation is necessary, and this is outside the scope of this book. The meaning of the individual flexibility and stiffness coefficients of complex linear systems is, however, considered below.

3. Flexibility of complex systems.

When a linear elastic system such as that represented in fig. VII.1 is subjected to a force or load, deflection of every point other than fixed supports occurs in general. Moreover, because of the nature of the

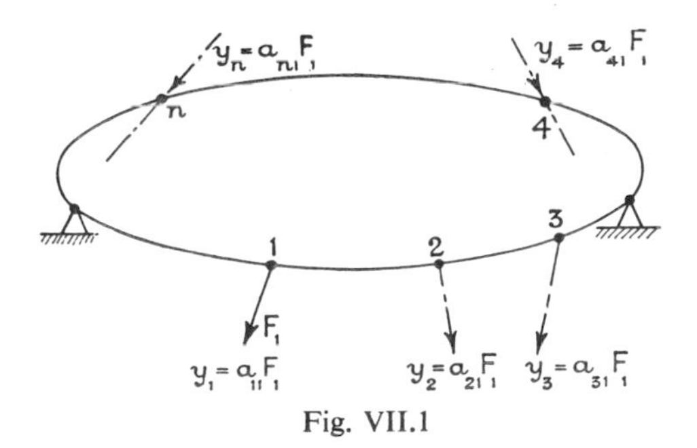

Fig. VII.1

system, the relationship between the force and any deflection at any point is linear. Thus, if the force is denoted by F_1 the deflection which it causes at its point of application in the direction of its line of action can be expressed as

$$y_1 = a_{11} F_1 \tag{VII.3}$$

where a_{11} is a constant coefficient of flexibility, being the deflection at point 1 in the direction of F_1 due to unit force applied instead of F_1. The first subscript denotes the location of the deflection, while the second denotes the location of the unit force. In this instance both are at the same point 1. Similarly, the deflection which F_1 causes in a specified direction at a point 2 can be expressed as

$$y_2 = a_{21}F_1 \tag{VII.4}$$

where the flexibility coefficient a_{21} is the deflection in the direction specified at point 2 due to unit load applied in the direction of F_1 at point 1, as indicated by the subscripts. For deflections at other points due to F_1 it is possible to write, therefore,

$$y_3 = a_{31}F_1 \;;\; y_4 = a_{41}F_1 \;;\; y_5 = a_{51}F_1 \;;\; \ldots \;;\; y_n = a_{n1}F_1 \tag{VII.5}$$

4. Deflections of complex systems in terms of loads and flexibility coefficients.

If, now, loads $F_1, F_2, F_3, F_4, \ldots, F_n$ are applied at points 1, 2, 3, 4, $\ldots, n$, respectively, as shown in fig. VII.2, the deflection of any point in a specified direction is, by the principle of superposition, the sum of the

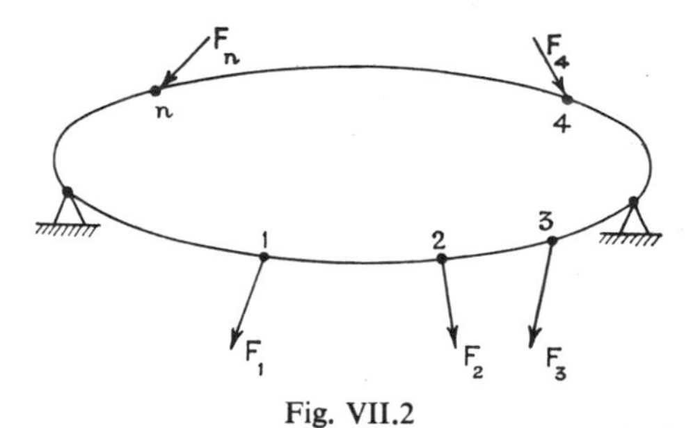

Fig. VII.2

deflections in that direction caused by each of the forces $F_1, F_2, F_3, F_4, \ldots, F_n$ acting separately. Thus, due to all of the loads acting together the deflections at the various points in the directions of the lines of action of the respective loads can be expressed as follows:

$$\begin{aligned}
y_1 &= a_{11}F_1 + a_{12}F_2 + a_{13}F_3 + a_{14}F_4 + \ldots + a_{1n}F_n \\
y_2 &= a_{21}F_1 + a_{22}F_2 + a_{23}F_3 + a_{24}F_4 + \ldots + a_{2n}F_n \\
y_3 &= a_{31}F_1 + a_{32}F_2 + a_{33}F_3 + a_{34}F_4 + \ldots + a_{3n}F_n \\
y_4 &= a_{41}F_1 + a_{42}F_2 + a_{43}F_3 + a_{44}F_4 + \ldots + a_{4n}F_n \\
&\cdots \\
y_n &= a_{n1}F_1 + a_{n2}F_2 + a_{n3}F_3 + a_{n4}F_4 + \ldots + a_{nn}F_n
\end{aligned} \tag{VII.6}$$

where the coefficients a_{21}, a_{31}, a_{41}, . . . , a_{n1} are as in equations (VII.4) and (VII.5), if the directions of the lines of action of the forces F_2, F_3, F_4, . . . , F_n are the same as the directions chosen for the deflections at points 2, 3, 4, . . . , n, respectively, in § 3 above. By the reciprocal theorem,

$$\begin{aligned} a_{12} = a_{21} \ ; \ a_{13} = a_{31} \ ; \ a_{14} = a_{41} \ ; \ . \ . \ . \ ; \ a_{1n} = a_{n1} \\ a_{23} = a_{32} \ ; \ a_{24} = a_{42} \ ; \ a_{25} = a_{52} \ ; \ . \ . \ . \ ; \ a_{2n} = a_{n2} \end{aligned} \qquad \text{(VII.7)}$$

or, in general,

$$a_{ij} = a_{ji} \qquad \text{(VII.8)}$$

that is, the deflection at point i in the direction of the line of action of the force at i due to unit force at point j is equal to the deflection at j in the direction of the line of action of the force at j due to unit force at i in this instance.

5. Calculation of flexibility coefficients.

If it is desired to make use of flexibility coefficients to set up equations for deflections of a system, it is, of course, necessary to calculate the values of the coefficients first of all. This can be done by considering unit loads to be applied to the system at the appropriate points and in the appropriate directions, in turn, and calculating the deflection of every such point due to each unit load. These calculations can if necessary be carried out using the principle of virtual work or the complementary-energy method.

6. Example of flexibility coefficients for a specific system.

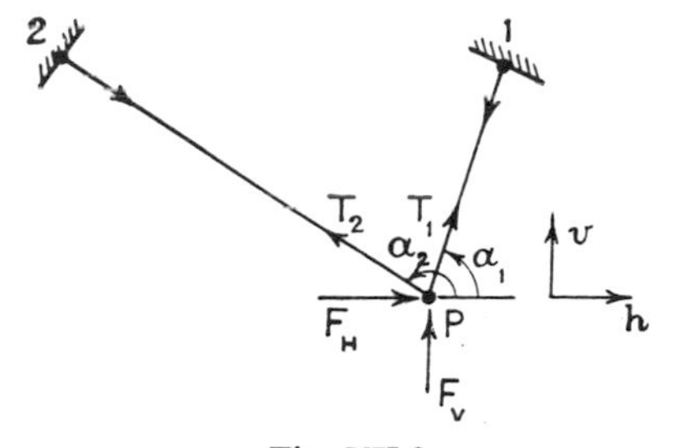

Fig. VII.3

The expressions for the deflections v and h of the joint P of the simple linear system shown in fig. VII.3 derived in Chapter V, § 3 (equation

V.14) by the complementary-energy method are as follows:

$$v = \frac{a_1 \cos^2 \alpha_2 + a_2 \cos^2 \alpha_1}{(\sin \alpha_1 \cos \alpha_2 - \cos \alpha_1 \sin \alpha_2)^2} F_V - \frac{a_1 \sin \alpha_2 \cos \alpha_2 + a_2 \sin \alpha_1 \cos \alpha_1}{(\sin \alpha_1 \cos \alpha_2 - \cos \alpha_1 \sin \alpha_2)^2} F_H$$

$$h = -\frac{a_1 \sin \alpha_2 \cos \alpha_2 + a_2 \sin \alpha_1 \cos \alpha_1}{(\sin \alpha_1 \cos \alpha_2 - \cos \alpha_1 \sin \alpha_2)^2} F_V + \frac{a_1 \sin^2 \alpha_2 + a_2 \sin^2 \alpha_1}{(\sin \alpha_1 \cos \alpha_2 - \cos \alpha_1 \sin \alpha_2)^2} F_H \quad \text{(VII.9)}$$

where a_1 and a_2 are the flexibilities of the members, respectively, and as noted there the coefficients F_V and F_H are flexibility coefficients of the system as follows:

$$\frac{a_1 \cos^2 \alpha_2 + a_2 \cos^2 \alpha_1}{(\sin \alpha_1 \cos \alpha_2 - \cos \alpha_1 \sin \alpha_2)^2} = a_{VV};$$

$$-\frac{a_1 \sin \alpha_2 \cos \alpha_2 + a_2 \sin \alpha_1 \cos \alpha_1}{(\sin \alpha_1 \cos \alpha_2 - \cos \alpha_1 \sin \alpha_2)^2} = a_{VH}$$

$$-\frac{a_1 \sin \alpha_2 \cos \alpha_2 + a_2 \sin \alpha_1 \cos \alpha_1}{(\sin \alpha_1 \cos \alpha_2 - \cos \alpha_1 \sin \alpha_2)^2} = a_{HV}; \quad \text{(VII.10)}$$

$$\frac{a_1 \sin^2 \alpha_2 + a_2 \sin^2 \alpha_1}{(\sin \alpha_1 \cos \alpha_2 - \cos \alpha_1 \sin \alpha_2)^2} = a_{HH}$$

where the subscripts V and H refer to the vertical and horizontal directions at P, respectively. Clearly $a_{VH} = a_{HV}$ in accordance with the reciprocal theorem. In this instance letter subscripts are used as being more descriptive, but their scheme is exactly as for the numerical kind described above.

7. Calculation of flexibility coefficients using virtual work.

The independent calculation of a_{VV}, $a_{VH} = a_{HV}$, and a_{HH} for the system considered in § 6 above can be achieved conveniently, as noted in § 5, with the aid of the principle of virtual work. Thus in order to find a_{VV} and a_{HV} it is necessary to consider unit vertical load acting at P, as shown in fig. VII.4*a*, and then calculate the vertical and horizontal deflections of P which this load causes. These deflections are a_{VV} and a_{HV} respectively.

Now, by the principle of virtual work,

$$1 \,.\, a_{VV} = T_1' e_1' + T_2' e_2' = a_1 T_1'^2 + a_2 T_2'^2$$

and

$$1 \,.\, a_{HV} = T_1'' e_1' + T_2'' e_2' = a_1 T_1' T_1'' + a_2 T_2' T_2'' \quad \text{(VII.11)}$$

where T_1' and T_2' and e_1' and e_2' are the forces in the members, and their changes in length, respectively, due to unit vertical load, and T_1'' and T_2'' are the forces in the members, respectively, due to unit horizontal load

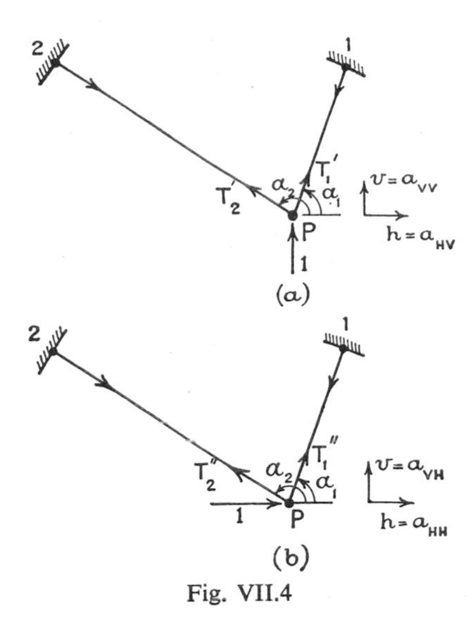

Fig. VII.4

(fig. VII.4*b*). By resolving forces vertically and horizontally at P, the following values of these forces are obtained, tension being positive:

$$T_1' = \frac{-\cos\alpha_2}{\sin\alpha_1\cos\alpha_2 - \cos\alpha_1\sin\alpha_2}; \quad T_2' = \frac{\cos\alpha_1}{\sin\alpha_1\cos\alpha_2 - \cos\alpha_1\sin\alpha_2} \tag{VII.12}$$

$$T_1'' = \frac{\sin\alpha_2}{\sin\alpha_1\cos\alpha_2 - \cos\alpha_1\sin\alpha_2}; \quad T_2'' = \frac{-\sin\alpha_1}{\sin\alpha_1\cos\alpha_2 - \cos\alpha_1\sin\alpha_2}$$

and since $e_1' = a_1 T_1'$ and $e_2' = a_2 T_2'$

$$e_1' = \frac{-a_1\cos\alpha_2}{\sin\alpha_1\cos\alpha_2 - \cos\alpha_1\sin\alpha_2}; \quad e_2' = \frac{a_2\cos\alpha_1}{\sin\alpha_1\cos\alpha_2 - \cos\alpha_1\sin\alpha_2} \tag{VII.13}$$

Substituting in equations (VII.11), therefore,

$$\begin{aligned} a_{VV} &= \frac{a_1\cos^2\alpha_2 + a_2\cos^2\alpha_1}{(\sin\alpha_1\cos\alpha_2 - \cos\alpha_1\sin\alpha_2)^2} \\ a_{HV} &= -\frac{a_1\sin\alpha_2\cos\alpha_2 + a_2\sin\alpha_1\cos\alpha_1}{(\sin\alpha_1\cos\alpha_2 - \cos\alpha_1\sin\alpha_2)^2} \end{aligned} \tag{VII.14}$$

which are identical to the corresponding expressions in equations (VII.10).

Again, consideration of unit horizontal load at P, as shown in fig.

VII.4*b*, and finding the resulting horizontal and vertical deflections gives a_{HH} and a_{VH}, respectively. Thus, by the principle of virtual work,

$$\begin{aligned} 1 \,.\, a_{HH} &= T_1'' e_1'' + T_2'' e_2'' = a_1 T_1''^2 + a_2 T_2''^2 \\ 1 \,.\, a_{VH} &= T_1' e_1'' + T_2'' e_2'' = a_1 T_1' T_1'' + a_2 T_2' T_2'' \end{aligned} \qquad \text{(VII.15)}$$

from which by comparison with equations (VII.11) it is immediately clear that $a_{VH} = a_{HV}$. Substitution for T_1'' and T_2'' from equations (VII.12) in the first of equations (VII.15) gives

$$a_{HH} = \frac{a_1 \sin^2 \alpha_2 + a_2 \sin^2 \alpha_1}{(\sin \alpha_1 \cos \alpha_2 - \cos \alpha_1 \sin \alpha_2)^2} \qquad \text{(VII.16)}$$

which again is identical to the corresponding expression in equations (VII.10).

8. Compatibility equations for statically-indeterminate systems in terms of flexibility coefficients.

If the structure has a redundant member as shown in fig. VII.5, the equation for the compatibility of the strain of this member and the statically-determinate system can be written directly using flexibility

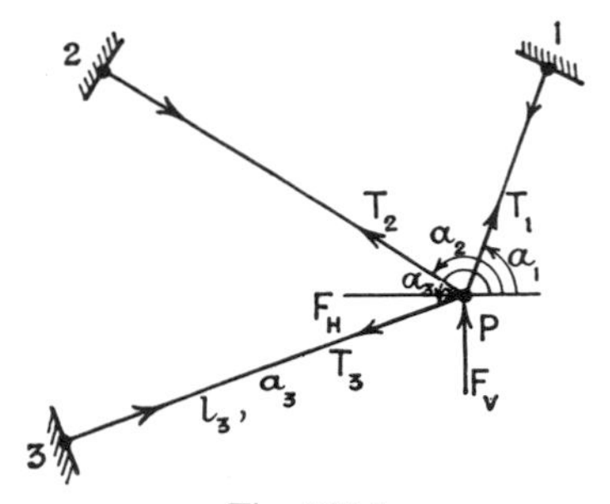

Fig. VII.5

coefficients. Assuming that the force T_3 in the redundant member is tensile and considering it as an additional load on the statically-determinate system, the deflection of this system in the line of the redundant member is

$$e_3 = a_{33} T_3 + a_{3V} F_V + a_{3H} F_H \qquad \text{(VII.17)}$$

in the sense of T_3, where the subscript 3 denotes the line of the redundant member. But the change in length of the redundant member itself is $a_3 T_3$ and corresponds to an increase in length, because T_3 is assumed to be tensile. If the unstrained length of the redundant member is l_3 and is the same as the length of the line of this member in the unloaded statically-determinate system, then for compatibility of the strains

$$l_3 - e_3 = l_3 + a_3 T_3$$

or

$$e_3 + a_3 T_3 = 0 \tag{VII.18}$$

Therefore, substitution from equation (VII.17) gives

$$(a_3 + a_{33}) T_3 + a_{3V} F_V + a_{3H} F_H = 0 \tag{VII.19}$$

This equation is equivalent to equation (V.26) which, when the terms are regrouped, is as follows:

$$\left[a_3 + \frac{a_1(\cos\alpha_2 \sin\alpha_3 - \sin\alpha_2 \cos\alpha_3)^2 + a_2(\cos\alpha_1 \sin\alpha_3 - \sin\alpha_1 \cos\alpha_3)^2}{(\sin\alpha_1 \cos\alpha_2 - \cos\alpha_1 \sin\alpha_2)^2}\right] T_3 +$$

$$+\left[\frac{a_1 \cos\alpha_2 (\cos\alpha_2 \sin\alpha_3 - \sin\alpha_2 \cos\alpha_3) + a_2 \cos\alpha_1 (\cos\alpha_1 \sin\alpha_3 - \sin\alpha_1 \cos\alpha_3)}{(\sin\alpha_1 \cos\alpha_2 - \cos\alpha_1 \sin\alpha_2)^2}\right] F_V +$$

$$-\left[\frac{a_1 \sin\alpha_2 (\cos\alpha_2 \sin\alpha_3 - \sin\alpha_2 \cos\alpha_3) + a_2 \sin\alpha_1 (\cos\alpha_1 \sin\alpha_3 - \sin\alpha_1 \cos\alpha_3)}{(\sin\alpha_1 \cos\alpha_2 - \cos\alpha_1 \sin\alpha_2)^2}\right] F_H$$

$$= 0 \tag{VII.20}$$

Clearly

$$a_{33} = \frac{a_1 (\cos\alpha_2 \sin\alpha_3 - \sin\alpha_2 \cos\alpha_3)^2 + a_2 (\cos\alpha_1 \sin\alpha_3 - \sin\alpha_1 \cos\alpha_3)^2}{(\sin\alpha_1 \cos\alpha_2 - \cos\alpha_1 \sin\alpha_2)^2}$$

$$a_{3V} = \frac{a_1 \cos\alpha_2 (\cos\alpha_2 \sin\alpha_3 - \sin\alpha_2 \cos\alpha_3) + a_2 \cos\alpha_1 (\cos\alpha_1 \sin\alpha_3 - \sin\alpha_1 \cos\alpha_3)}{(\sin\alpha_1 \cos\alpha_2 - \cos\alpha_1 \sin\alpha_2)^2} \tag{VII.21}$$

$$a_{3H} = -\frac{a_1 \sin\alpha_2 (\cos\alpha_2 \sin\alpha_3 - \sin\alpha_2 \cos\alpha_3) + a_2 \sin\alpha_1 (\cos\alpha_1 \sin\alpha_3 - \sin\alpha_1 \cos\alpha_3)}{(\sin\alpha_1 \cos\alpha_2 - \cos\alpha_1 \sin\alpha_2)^2}$$

9. Deflections of a statically-indeterminate system in terms of flexibility coefficients.

The deflections v and h of the joint P of the system shown in fig. VII.5 can also be written using the flexibility coefficients of the statically-determinate system as follows:

$$v = a_{VV} F_V + a_{VH} F_H + a_{V3} T_3$$

$$h = a_{HV} F_V + a_{HH} F_H + a_{H3} T_3 \tag{VII.22}$$

where a_{VV}, $a_{VH} = a_{HV}$, and a_{HH} are given by equations (VII.14) and (VII.16). Before these equations can be used, however, it is necessary to find T_3 by means of equation (VII.19).

Alternatively, the flexibility coefficients of the redundant system can be used, when the following equations are obtained:

$$v = a'_{VV} F_V + a'_{VH} F_H$$
$$h = a'_{HV} F_V + a'_{HH} F_H \qquad \text{(VII.23)}$$

where a'_{VV} is the deflection of joint P of the redundant system in the direction v due to unit load applied at P in the same direction; a'_{VH} is the deflection of joint P of the redundant system in the direction v due to unit load applied at P in the direction h; and similarly for $a'_{HV} = a'_{VH}$ and a'_{HH}.

The calculation of the flexibility coefficients of a redundant system is much more complicated than for a statically-determinate system, however, because it involves analysing the system for the unit forces which produce deflections which represent the required flexibility coefficients.

10. Loads on complex systems in terms of deflections and stiffness coefficients.

Equations (VII.6) can be inverted in the mathematical sense so that the loads are expressed in terms of the deflections as follows:

$$\begin{aligned}
F_1 &= b_{11} y_1 + b_{12} y_2 + b_{13} y_3 + b_{14} y_4 + \dots + b_{1n} y_n \\
F_2 &= b_{21} y_1 + b_{22} y_2 + b_{23} y_3 + b_{24} y_4 + \dots + b_{2n} y_n \\
F_3 &= b_{31} y_1 + b_{32} y_2 + b_{33} y_3 + b_{34} y_4 + \dots + b_{3n} y_n \\
F_4 &= b_{41} y_1 + b_{42} y_2 + b_{43} y_3 + b_{44} y_4 + \dots + b_{4n} y_n \qquad \text{(VII.24)} \\
&\cdots \\
&\cdots \\
F_n &= b_{n1} y_1 + b_{n2} y_2 + b_{n3} y_3 + b_{n4} y_4 + \dots + b_{nn} y_n
\end{aligned}$$

where b_{11}, b_{12}, b_{13}, etc., are the stiffness coefficients of the system and are defined in the following way:

b_{11} is the force at point 1 in the line of action of F_1 which is necessary to produce unit deflection in this direction at point 1 when the deflection of every other point is prevented.

b_{12} is the force at point 1 which is necessary to prevent deflection of point 1 in the line of action of F_1 when unit deflection at point 2 is produced by a force b_{22} in the line of action of F_2. At the same time the deflection of points 3, 4, 5, . . . , n is prevented by forces b_{32}, b_{42}, b_{52}, . . . , b_{n2}, respectively acting in the direction of F_3, F_4, F_5, . . . , F_n, respectively.

In general b_{ij} is the force at point i in the line of action of F_i which is necessary to prevent deflection of point i in this direction when unit deflection of point j is produced by a force b_{jj} acting in the line of action of F_{jj}. In accordance with the reciprocal theorem $b_{ij} = b_{ji}$.

For a linear system with a single degree of freedom, such as a simple spring, the stiffness coefficient is merely the reciprocal of the flexibility coefficient as noted in § 2 above, but for more complicated systems the stiffness coefficients cannot be found merely by inverting the individual flexibility coefficients.

11. Stiffness coefficients of a statically-indeterminate system.

In Chapter II, § 5, a redundant structure with linear characteristics similar to that shown in fig. VII.5 is used to illustrate the use of the strain-energy method as a means of setting up equations of equilibrium in terms of deflections and forces. The equations so obtained for this system are

$$F_V = (b_1 \sin^2\alpha_1 + b_2 \sin^2\alpha_2 + b_3 \sin^2\alpha_3)v + (b_1 \sin\alpha_1 \cos\alpha_1 + b_2 \sin\alpha_2 \cos\alpha_2 + b_3 \sin\alpha_3 \cos\alpha_3)\,h$$

$$F_H = (b_1 \sin\alpha_1 \cos\alpha_1 + b_2 \sin\alpha_2 \cos\alpha_2 + b_3 \sin\alpha_3 \cos\alpha_3)v + (b_1 \cos^2\alpha_1 + b_2 \cos^2\alpha_2 + b_3 \cos^2\alpha_3)\,h \qquad \text{(VII.25)}$$

where v and h are the deflections of the joint P and b_1, b_2, and b_3 are the stiffnesses or forces per unit change in length of the members, respectively. As noted in Chapter II, § 6, the quantities in the brackets are stiffness coefficients of the system. Thus

$$b_1 \sin^2\alpha_1 + b_2 \sin^2\alpha_2 + b_3 \sin^2\alpha_3 = b_{VV}$$

$$b_1 \sin\alpha_1 \cos\alpha_1 + b_2 \sin\alpha_2 \cos\alpha_2 + b_3 \sin\alpha_3 \cos\alpha_3 = b_{VH} = b_{HV} \qquad \text{(VII.26)}$$

$$b_1 \cos^2\alpha_1 + b_2 \cos^2\alpha_2 + b_3 \cos^2\alpha_3 = b_{HH}$$

and it is noted that $b_{VH} = b_{HV}$ in accordance with the reciprocal theorem. If there is no redundant member in the system it is merely necessary to put the stiffness of the redundant $b_3 = 0$ in equations (VII.26).

12. Calculation of stiffness coefficients.

In order to show how stiffness coefficients are derived from first principles it is convenient to consider the linear elastic system shown in fig. VII.5. If forces are applied so that P has unit vertical deflection but no horizontal deflection, as shown in fig. VII.6, these forces represent b_{VV} vertical and b_{HV} horizontal. They can be found by first finding the changes in length e_1^V, e_2^V, and e_3^V, respectively, of the members which are compatible with unit vertical displacement of P. Then the forces in the members can be found because $T_1^V = b_1 e_1^V$, $T_2^V = b_2 e_2^V$, and $T_3^V = b_3 e_3^V$, if b_1, b_2, and b_3 are the stiffnesses of the members, and finally b_{VV} and b_{HV} are obtained by resolving T_1^V, T_2^V, and T_3^V vertically and horizontally, respectively and considering the conditions of equilibrium. Thus

$$e_1^V = -1 \sin \alpha_1 \quad ; \quad e_2^V = -1 \sin \alpha_2 \quad ; \quad e_3^V = -1 \sin \alpha_3 \qquad \text{(VII.27)}$$

where the minus sign denotes compressive straining or shortening of the members. Therefore

$$T_1^V = -b_1 \sin \alpha_1 \quad ; \quad T_2^V = -b_2 \sin \alpha_2 \quad ; \quad T_3^V = -b_3 \sin \alpha_3 \qquad \text{(VII.28)}$$

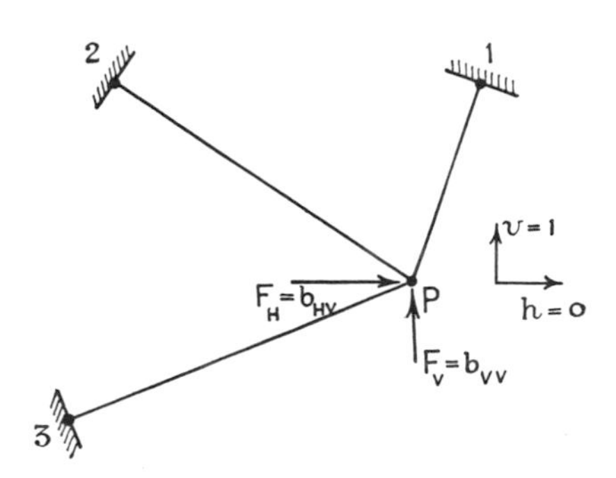

Fig. VII.6

and for equilibrium

$$-b_{VV} = T_1^V \sin \alpha_1 + T_2^V \sin \alpha_2 + T_3^V \sin \alpha_3 = -b_1 \sin^2 \alpha_1 - b_2 \sin^2 \alpha_2 - b_3 \sin^2 \alpha_3$$

$$-b_{HV} = -T_1^V \cos \alpha_1 + T_2^V \cos \alpha_2 + T_3^V \cos \alpha_3 = -b_1 \sin \alpha_1 \cos \alpha_1 - b_2 \sin \alpha_2 \cos \alpha_2 - b_3 \sin \alpha_3 \cos \alpha_3$$

or

$$\left.\begin{aligned} b_{VV} &= b_1 \sin^2 \alpha_1 + b_2 \sin^2 \alpha_2 + b_3 \sin^2 \alpha_3 \\ b_{HV} &= b_1 \sin \alpha_1 \cos \alpha_1 + b_2 \sin \alpha_2 \cos \alpha_2 + b_3 \sin \alpha_3 \cos \alpha_3 \end{aligned}\right\} \qquad \text{(VII.29)}$$

If, now, the horizontal deflection of P is unity and the vertical deflection is zero, the forces applied at P to achieve this are b_{HH} and b_{VH}. In order to find b_{HH} and b_{VH} by the same procedure as before,

$$e_1^H = -1 . \cos \alpha_1 \,; \quad e_2^H = -1 . \cos \alpha_2 \,; \quad e_3^H = -1 . \cos \alpha_3 \qquad \text{(VII.30)}$$

so that

$$T_1^H = -b_1 \cos \alpha_1 \,; \quad T_2^H = -b_2 \cos \alpha_2 \,; \quad T_3^H = -b_3 \cos \alpha_3 \qquad \text{(VII.31)}$$

and for equilibrium

$$-b_{HH} = T_1^H \cos\alpha_1 + T_2^H \cos\alpha_2 + T_3^H \cos\alpha_3 = -b_1 \cos^2\alpha_1 - b_2 \cos^2\alpha_2 - b_3 \cos^2\alpha_3$$

$$-b_{VH} = T_1^H \sin\alpha_1 + T_2^H \sin\alpha_2 + T_3^H \sin\alpha_3 = -b_1 \sin\alpha_1 \cos\alpha - b_2 \sin\alpha_2 \cos\alpha_2 - b_3 \sin\alpha_3 \cos\alpha_3$$

or

$$b_{HH} = b_1 \cos^2\alpha_1 + b_2 \cos^2\alpha_2 + b_3 \cos^2\alpha_3 \qquad \text{(VII.32)}$$

$$b_{VH} = b_1 \sin\alpha_1 \cos\alpha_1 + b_2 \sin\alpha_2 \cos\alpha_2 + b_3 \sin\alpha_3 \cos\alpha_3$$

Clearly $b_{VH} = b_{HV}$ in accordance with the reciprocal theorem, and all the coefficients are identical to those given in equations (VII.26) and derived by the strain-energy method.

It should be noted that the calculation of the individual stiffness coefficients is easier than the calculation of the flexibility coefficients for this example, and this is usually the case. Moreover, it is clear that the presence of redundant members does not complicate the calculation of the stiffness coefficients very much.

13. Equations of equilibrium in terms of deflections and stiffness coefficients.

Once the stiffness coefficients of a system have been calculated, the equations of equilibrium can be set up and the deflections of the system found by solving these equations. Thus for the example considered above, the equations of equilibrium of joint P, the only free joints are

$$F_V = b_{VV} \, . \, v + b_{VH} \, . \, h$$
$$F_H = b_{HV} \, . \, v + b_{HH} \, . \, h \qquad \text{(equation II.20)}$$

which are linear simultaneous equations in v and h. Having found v and h, the changes in length e of the members can be calculated by resolving v and h in their lines, respectively. Thus

$$e_1 = -v \sin\alpha_1 - h \cos\alpha_1$$
$$e_2 = -v \sin\alpha_2 - h \cos\alpha_2 \qquad \text{(equation II.16)}$$
$$e_3 = -v \sin\alpha_3 - h \cos\alpha_3$$

and the forces in the members can be found because $T_1 = b_1 e_1$, $T_2 = b_2 e_2$, and $T_3 = b_3 e_3$. The form of equations (II.20) and this procedure is clearly independent of the number of redundant members.

14. Choice of method of analysis of statically-indeterminate systems.

When flexibility or stiffness coefficients are used for setting up the final simultaneous equations for the analysis of linear statically-indeterminate systems, instead of the complementary-energy method and the strain- or potential-energy methods, respectively, the number of these equations depends upon the factors considered in Chapter II, § 7; Chapter IV, § 10; and Chapter V, § 7 respectively; that is, by using flexibility coefficients the final equations are the conditions for the compatibility of the strains of the statically-determinate system and the redundant members, while by using stiffness coefficients the final equations are the conditions of equilibrium of the joints. The former are as numerous as the redundants, while the latter are as numerous as the degrees of freedom or independent components of deflection of joints. If there are fewer redundants than components of deflection of joints, the flexibility-coefficient procedure will lead to fewer final simultaneous equations than the stiffness-coefficient procedure and vice versa. As mentioned in Chapter II, § 7, this is an important factor in choosing which of the two approaches to use, because the solution of simultaneous equations is usually laborious.

Account must also be taken, however, of the labour necessary for calculating the flexibility and the stiffness coefficients, respectively. This is because, owing to the relative ease with which the latter are obtained, the stiffness-coefficient approach might well be the more advantageous when the redundants are equal in number to the components of deflection, and also when they exceed the number of components of deflection by only one or two.

Because when either the flexibility-coefficient method or the stiffness-coefficient method is used much of the work (that of finding the coefficients) can be split up into separate parts, these methods have much to commend them in comparison with the relevant energy methods. The latter retain their advantages, however, for dealing with continuous systems by approximation.

15. The reciprocal theorem.

After quoting the reciprocal theorem for linear elastic systems a number of times in this and previous chapters it is perhaps appropriate that detailed consideration of this theorem should be given. The expression of the theorem due to E. Betti is the form which is probably the most useful to engineers:

$$\sum_{1}^{n} F_i y_i' = \sum_{1}^{n} F_i' y_i \tag{VII.33}$$

where the set of applied forces or loads $F_1, F_2, F_3, \ldots, F_n$, acting upon a linear elastic system such as is shown in fig. VII.7, cause deflections $y_1, y_2, y_3, \ldots, y_n$, respectively, at their points of application in the direction of the lines of action of an alternative set of forces F'_1, F'_2, $F'_3, \ldots, F'_n$, which, when they replace the set $F_1, F_2, F_3, \ldots, F_n$, cause deflections $y'_1, y'_2, y'_3, \ldots, y'_n$, in the directions of the lines of action of $F_1, F_2, F_3, \ldots, F_n$, respectively. The points of application denoted by $1, 2, 3, \ldots, n$, are of course common to both sets of loads.

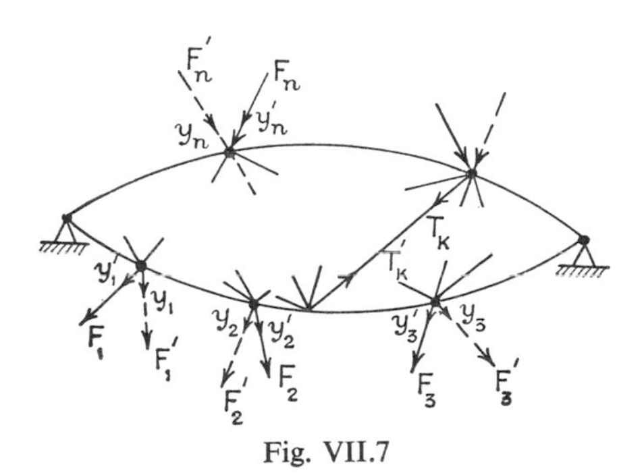

Fig. VII.7

In order to see what equation (VII.33) means in terms of flexibility coefficients it is convenient to suppose that all of the forces of the first set are zero except F_i and also that all of the forces of the second set are zero except F'_j, so that substitution in equation (VII.33) gives

$$F_i y'_i = F'_j y_j \tag{VII.34}$$

Now y'_i and y_j can be expressed in terms of flexibility coefficients as follows:

$$y'_i = a_{ij} F'_j$$

and

$$y_j = a_{ji} F_i \tag{VII.35}$$

where a_{ij} is the deflection at i in the direction of the line of action of F_i due to unit load applied at j in the direction of the line of action of F'_j; and a_{ji} is the deflection at j in the direction of the line of action of F'_j due to unit load applied at i in the direction of the line of action of F_i.*

Substitution for y'_i and y_j from equations (VII.35) in equation (VII.34) gives

$$a_{ij} F_i F'_j = a_{ji} F_i F'_j \tag{VII.36}$$

or

$$a_{ij} = a_{ji} \tag{VII.37}$$

* Compare these flexibility coefficients with those of § 4.

That means that a force F_i applied at point i of a linear elastic system causes a deflection at another point j in the direction of the line of action of the force F_j applied at j, which is equal to the deflection at point i in the direction of the line of action of F_i which is caused by a force F_j applied at j, equal in magnitude to F_i. In a similar way it can be shown that the stiffness coefficients b_{ij} and b_{ji} are identical.

16. Proof of the reciprocal theorem by virtual work.

Equation (VII.33) which expresses the reciprocal theorem can be proved conveniently with the aid of the principle of virtual work. If the elastic system consists of an assemblage of pin-jointed members, then the deflections y are compatible with changes in length e of the members, and the deflections y' are compatible with changes in length e' of the members. If the forces in the members due to the loads F are denoted by T, while those due to the loads F' are denoted by T', by the principle of virtual work,

$$\sum_1^n F_i y_i' = \sum_1^N T_k e_k'$$

and

$$\sum_1^n F_i' y_i = \sum_1^N T_k' e_k \tag{VII.38}$$

where N is the number of members in the system and the subscript k denotes any one member. The compatible sets of displacements y_1', y_2', $y_3', \ldots, y_n'$ and e_1', e_2', $e_3', \ldots, e_N'$ and $y_1, y_2, y_3, \ldots, y_n$ and e_1, e_2, $e_3, \ldots, e_N$ fulfil the condition whereby the magnitude of virtual displacements must be such that no significant change of geometry of the system is implied, simply because it is postulated that the system is linear. Geometrical distortion would cause non-linearity even if the members of the system themselves retained their linear characteristics. Now

$$e_k' = a_k T_k'$$

and

$$e_k = a_k T_k \tag{VII.39}$$

where a_k is the flexibility of an individual member. Substitution of these expressions for e_k' and e_k in equations (VII.38) gives

$$\sum_1^n F_i y_i' = \sum_1^N a_k T_k T_k'$$

and

$$\sum_1^n F_i' y_i = \sum_1^N a_k T_k T_k' \tag{VII.40}$$

therefore

$$\sum_1^n F_i\, y_i' = \sum_1^n F_i'\, y_i \qquad \text{(equation VII.34)}$$

which is Betti's form of the reciprocal theorem.

17. General conditions for linearity.

Finally, it is important to review carefully what is meant by a linear system. This might seem to be the way to begin the chapter rather than to end it, but there is always a danger that when deeper considerations are given too soon they are overlooked. For a system to have chacteristics linear in accordance with Hooke's law, not only must the individual parts or members of the system be linear but the members must act together in such a way that the system as a whole is linear. This means that the applied forces or loads must not cause significant change in the geometrical form of the system; that is, the deflections must be small in comparison with any dimension of the system. Otherwise, even if the members themselves retain their linearity, the characteristics of the system as a whole will be non-linear, as noted in § 16.

VIII Approximate Solutions using Energy Principles

1. Introduction.

The stationary properties of potential energy (law of conservation of energy) and complementary energy relating to fulfilment of conditions of equilibrium and compatibility of strains, respectively, afford means of obtaining approximate solutions for systems incorporating continua. Among those systems are continuous beams on elastic supports, grillages (interconnected beams), and suspension bridges. Moreover, it is possible to obtain upper and lower bound solutions to any such problems by applying the potential and complementary (approximate) methods in turn. The essence of the procedure for obtaining an approximate solution by the stationary potential-energy principle is the choice of a function (or series of functions) which can represent the distribution of deflection or strain of the system due to specified applied forces, and evaluating the parameters by equations derived from the energy principle. The geometrical boundary conditions of the system must be satisfied by the function, otherwise the behaviour in respect of deflection or strain is misrepresented at locations (boundaries) where it is defined without question by specified conditions. Similarly, the choice of a function which can represent the distribution of statically-indeterminate forces or bending moment enables the parameters to be found by equations derived from the stationary complementary-energy principle. The function chosen must, however, be such that specified conditions of statical equilibrium are satisfied.

Because it is easier to visualize the nature of the deflection or strain of a system due to specified forces or loads, it is frequently desirable to obtain an approximate solution using the potential-energy principle first of all. Then, that solution can be used to provide a basis for selecting a function or functions to represent force or bending moment distribution for the purpose of using the complementary-energy principle to obtain an alternative solution. Comparison of the two solutions will usually provide a basis for assessing their accuracy on an upper and lower bound basis as shown below.

The physical reasoning underlying the upper and lower bound theory is that the assumption of a distribution of deflection or strain implies the introduction of artificial restraints upon the system, while assumption of a distribution of statically-indeterminate force or bending moment implies relaxation of connections or continuity. Thus the approximate values of deflections at points of application of external forces, found by the potential-energy method will generally be less than the correct values due to the implicitly imposed restraints whereby the stiffness of the system is increased and it is made to behave somewhat differently from its natural manner. Again, the salient values of statically-indeterminate force or bending moment found approximately by the complementary-energy method will generally be less than the correct values due to the implication of relaxation of connections and reduction in stiffness of the system. Salient values of deflections calculated using the approximately determined force or bending moment distributions will generally be greater than the correct values. Also the salient values of the force or bending moment distribution consistent with the deflection or strain pattern determined approximately by the potential-energy procedure, will generally be greater than the correct values.

The approximate methods of solution afforded by energy principles are a major source of interest in those principles by engineering practitioners. In the following paragraphs the twofold approach to approximate solutions is demonstrated using a relatively simple statically-indeterminate system.

2. The problem.

A uniform beam of flexural rigidity EI and length $6l$, simply supported on rigid plinths at each end and by intermediate elastic supports of flexibility $a = kl^3/EI$ at intervals l apart, is subjected to a concentrated force F acting downward at the mid point of the beam. The deflections Δ and distribution of statically-indeterminate bending moment and forces are to be found.

The forces exerted by the intermediate elastic supports R_1, R_2,..., R_5 are clearly statically-indeterminate and, having regard to the symmetry of the system (Fig. VIII.1), $R_1 = R_5$ and $R_2 = R_4$.

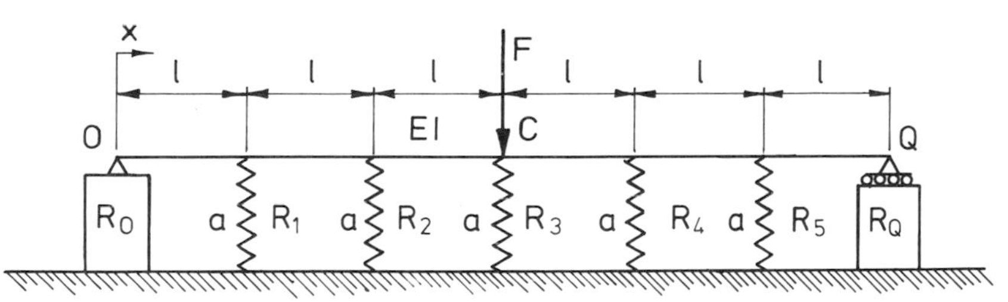

Fig. VIII.1

3. Exact solution.

The problem may be solved exactly using the following equations for the compatibility of deflections of the beam and elastic supports:

$$\Delta_1 = R_1(a_{11}+a_{15})+R_2(a_{12}+a_{14})+(R_3-F)a_{13} = -aR_1 \quad \text{(VIII.1)}$$

$$\Delta_2 = R_1(a_{21}+a_{25})+R_2(a_{22}+a_{24})+(R_3-F)a_{23} = -aR_2 \quad \text{(VIII.2)}$$

$$\Delta_3 = R_1(a_{31}+a_{35})+R_2(a_{32}+a_{34})+(R_3-F)a_{33} = -aR_3 \quad \text{(VIII.3)}$$

in which account of symmetry has been taken to reduce the equations from five (the number of statically-indeterminate quantities) to three, and in which account has been taken of the relevant conditions of equilibrium. The symbols are defined as follows:

Δ_1 ($= \Delta_5$), Δ_2 ($= \Delta_4$), and Δ_3 are the deflections of the beam and elastic supports at those supports.

a_{11} is the deflection of the simple beam at point 1 due to unit vertical force acting there (i.e. in the absence of the elastic supports throughout).

a_{15} is the deflection of the simple beam at point 1 due to unit vertical force acting at point 5.

a_{12}, a_{13}, a_{14}, and the other flexibility coefficients of the simple beam are defined similarly.

The term $R_1(a_{11}+a_{15})$ represents the effect at point 1 of the force R_1 acting there together with the effect at that point of $R_5 = R_1$ acting at point 5. The other terms of the equations may be justified in a similar manner while $-aR_1$, $-aR_2$, and $-aR_3$ represent the deflections of the elastic supports due to the forces acting upon them. The minus signs denote that those deflections are opposite in sense to the reactive forces exerted by those supports because it is the reactive effects, i.e. forces acting upon the beam, which appear in the equations.

The values of the flexibility coefficients may be found using the relationship for a uniform simply supported beam:

$$a_{PQ} = a_{QP} = \frac{p(L-q)}{6LEI}[2qL-(p^2+q^2)]$$

where L is now the length of the beam and p and q are the distances of the points P and Q, respectively, from the origin at the end of O of the beam (see reference 27 of the Bibliography). Thus:

$$a_{11} = \frac{l(6l-l)(2\times l\times 6l-2l^2)}{6\times 6l\times EI} = \frac{50l^3}{36EI}$$

$$a_{22} = \frac{2l(6l-2l)(2\times 2l\times 6l-8l^2)}{6\times 6l\times EI} = \frac{128l^3}{36EI}$$

$$a_{33} = \frac{3l(6l-3l)(2\times 3l\times 6l-18l^2)}{6\times 6l\times EI} = \frac{162l^3}{36EI}$$

$$a_{13} = a_{31} = \frac{l(6l-3l)(2\times 3l\times 6l-10l^2)}{6\times 6l\times EI} = \frac{78l^3}{36EI}$$

$$a_{12} = a_{21} = \frac{l(6l-2l)(2\times 2l\times 6l-5l^2)}{6\times 6l\times EI} = \frac{76l^3}{36EI}$$

$$a_{14} = a_{41} = \frac{l(6l-4l)(2\times 4l\times 6l-17l^2)}{6\times 6l\times EI} = \frac{62l^3}{36EI}$$

$$a_{15} = a_{51} = \frac{l(6l-5l)(2\times 5l\times 6l-26l^2)}{6\times 6l\times EI} = \frac{34l^3}{36EI}$$

$$a_{23} = a_{32} = \frac{2l(6l-3l)(2\times 3l\times 6l-13l^2)}{6\times 6l\times EI} = \frac{138l^3}{36EI}$$

$$a_{24} = a_{42} = \frac{2l(6l-4l)(2\times 4l\times 6l-20l^2)}{6\times 6l\times EI} = \frac{112l^3}{36EI}$$

also: $a_{34} = a_{43} = a_{23} = a_{32}$; $a_{35} = a_{53} = a_{13} = a_{31}$;

$a_{52} = a_{25} = a_{14} = a_{41}$.

Substituting these values of the flexibility coefficients in equations (VIII.1) to (VIII.3) and putting $a = \alpha l^3/36EI$ (where $\alpha = 36k$):

$$(84+\alpha)R_1+138R_2+78R_3 = 78F \quad \text{(VIII.4)}$$

$$138R_1+(240+\alpha)R_2+138R_3 = 138F \quad \text{(VIII.5)}$$

$$156R_1+276R_2+(162+\alpha)R_3 = 162F \quad \text{(VIII.6)}$$

If, for example, $k = 5$ then $\alpha = 180$ and:

$$44R_1+23R_2+13R_3 = 13F \quad \text{(VIII.7)}$$

$$23R_1+70R_2+23R_3 = 23F \quad \text{(VIII.8)}$$

$$26R_1+46R_2+57R_3 = 27F \quad \text{(VIII.9)}$$

whence: $R_1 = 0{\cdot}113F$; $R_2 = 0{\cdot}210F$; $R_3 = 0{\cdot}248F$

$(R_0 = 0{\cdot}053F)$

therefore:

$$\Delta_1 = aR_1 = 0{\cdot}565l^3/EI; \quad \Delta_2 = aR_2 = 1{\cdot}050l^3/EI;$$

$$\Delta_3 = aR_3 = 1{\cdot}240l^3/EI$$

and, by statics: $M_{\max} = 0{\cdot}595lF$

4. Potential energy or conservation of energy solution.

The energy quantities involved are the strain energy (U) of the beam and intermediate elastic supports and the work done (W) by the external force F. The condition for stationary potential energy (V) is:

$$\delta V = \delta U - \delta W = 0 \qquad \text{(VIII.10)}$$

which is equivalent to the condition $\delta U = \delta W$ for conservation of energy in respect of a small variation of the deflections or strains of the system.

Now an increment of strain energy of a beam associated with bending is $M\,\delta\phi$ per unit length of the beam, where M is the bending moment and $\delta\phi$ is the infinitesimally small angle through which unit length of the beam bends due to a small increment δM of M. Thus for the whole of the beam:

$$\delta U_b = \int_0^{6l} [M\,\delta\phi]\,dx \qquad \text{(VIII.11)}$$

and since, by the elementary (linearly elastic) theory of bending, $\dfrac{M}{I} = \dfrac{E}{R}$

where $\dfrac{1}{R} \doteqdot \dfrac{d^2\Delta}{dx^2}$, $M = EI\dfrac{d^2\Delta}{dx^2}$, and $\delta\phi = \delta\left(\dfrac{1}{R}\right) = \delta\left(\dfrac{d^2\Delta}{dx^2}\right)$

so that:

$$\delta U_b = EI\int_0^{6l} \left[\left(\frac{d^2\Delta}{dx^2}\right)\delta\left(\frac{d^2\Delta}{dx^2}\right)\right] dx \qquad \text{(VIII.12)}$$

while for an elastic support:

$$\delta U_i = R_i\,\delta\Delta_i = \frac{1}{a}(\Delta_i\,\delta\Delta_i) \qquad \text{(VIII.13)}$$

so that the total increment of strain energy is:

$$\delta U = \delta U_b + \sum^{5} \delta U_i = EI\int_0^{6l} \left[\left(\frac{d^2\Delta}{dx^2}\right)\delta\left(\frac{d^2\Delta}{dx^2}\right)\right] dx + \frac{1}{a}\sum^{5} \Delta_i\,\delta\Delta_i \qquad \text{(VIII.14)}$$

Again an increment of work done δW by the external force, corresponding with δU is:

$$\delta W = F\,\delta\Delta_3 \qquad \text{(VIII.15)}$$

Now the simplest assumption in respect of deflection of the beam consistent with the geometrical boundary conditions $\Delta = 0$ at $x = 0$ and $x = 6l$, is:

$$\Delta = A \sin\frac{\pi}{6l}x \qquad \text{(VIII.16)}$$

Substituting that in equations (VIII.14) and (VIII.15) and using equation (VIII.10) gives:

$$\delta U = EI\left(\frac{\pi}{6l}\right)^4 A\,\delta A \int_0^{6l} \sin^2\frac{\pi}{6l}\times dx + \frac{1}{a}\left[\left(2\times\frac{1}{2^2}\right) + 2\times\left(\frac{\sqrt{3}}{2}\right)^2 + 1\right] A\,\delta A$$

$$= \delta W = F\,\delta A \qquad \text{(VIII.17)}$$

or:
$$\frac{EI}{l^3}\left(\frac{\pi^4}{2\times 6^3}+\frac{3}{k}\right)A = F$$

whence:
$$A = \frac{Fl^3}{EI}\left(\frac{k}{0{\cdot}225k+3}\right) \tag{VIII.18}$$

If $k = 5$ then:
$$A = 1{\cdot}213\,\frac{Fl^3}{EI}$$

and
$$\Delta = 1{\cdot}213\,\frac{Fl^3}{EI}\sin\frac{\pi}{6l}x$$

whence:
$$R_1 = \Delta_1/a = 0{\cdot}121F$$
$$R_2 = \Delta_2/a = 0{\cdot}210F$$
$$R_3 = \Delta_3/a = 0{\cdot}242F$$
$$(R_0 = 0{\cdot}048F)$$

and by statics:
$$M_{\text{max}} = 0{\cdot}596lF \quad \text{(at the centre of the beam)}$$

In this instance the function chosen as a possible suitable representation of the deflection of the beam has one parameter only. In general, however, it is necessary to include more than one parameter as, for example, $A_1 \sin\frac{\pi}{6l}x + A_2 \sin\frac{3\pi}{6l}x$ in this particular symmetrical problem, if the beam is very flexible relative to the elastic supports. Sufficient equations may then be obtained by partial differentiation with respect to the parameters, thus

$$\frac{\partial V}{\partial A_1} = 0 \quad\text{or}\quad \frac{\partial U}{\partial A_1} = \frac{\partial W}{\partial A_1}$$
$$\frac{\partial V}{\partial A_2} = 0 \quad\text{or}\quad \frac{\partial U}{\partial A_2} = \frac{\partial W}{\partial A_2} \tag{VIII.19}$$

It is, however, pointless to choose functions for an approximate solution such that the unknown parameters are as numerous or nearly as numerous as the unknowns which would appear in an exact solution, that is, three in this instance.

5. Complementary energy solution.

The complementary energy consists of that of the beam together with that of the elastic supports. The increment of complementary energy of a beam is $\phi\,\delta M$ per unit length if ϕ is the angle through which unit length bends. For the whole beam, then:

$$\delta C_b = \int_0^{6l} [\phi\,\delta M]\,dx \tag{VIII.20}$$

and putting $\phi = \frac{1}{R} = \frac{M}{EI}$ by the elementary theory of bending:

$$\delta C_b = \frac{1}{EI}\int_0^{6l} [M\,\delta M]\,dx \qquad \text{(VIII.21)}$$

Then an increment of complementary energy of an elastic support is:

$$\delta C_i = \Delta_i\,\delta R_i = aR_i\,\delta R_i \qquad \text{(VIII.22)}$$

so that the total increment of complementary energy is:

$$\delta C = \delta C_b + \sum^5 \delta C_i = \frac{1}{EI}\int_0^{6l} [M\,\delta M]\,dx + a\sum^5 R_i\,\delta R_i \qquad \text{(VIII.23)}$$

Assuming* now (guided by the potential energy solution) that:

$$M = Bx^3 \quad \text{from } x = 0 \text{ to } 3l \qquad \text{(VIII.24)}$$

as satisfying the boundary conditions of equilibrium it is possible to express R_i in terms of B thus:

$$\begin{aligned}
\text{at } x = l \quad & M = Bl^3 = R_0\,l \\
& \therefore\ R_0 = Bl^2 \\
\text{at } x = 2l \quad & M = 8Bl^3 = 2R_0\,l + R_1\,l \\
& \therefore\ R_1 = 6Bl^2 \\
\text{at } x = 3l \quad & M = 27Bl^3 = 3R_0\,l + 2R_1\,l + R_2\,l \\
& \therefore\ R_2 = 12Bl^2
\end{aligned}$$

also

$$\begin{aligned}
F &= 2(R_0 + R_1 + R_2) + R_3 \\
\therefore\ R_3 &= F - 38Bl^2
\end{aligned}$$

Now by the principle of stationary complementary energy:

$$\frac{dC}{dB} = \frac{2}{EI}\int_0^{3l} M\frac{dM}{dB}\,dx + 2a\left(R_1\frac{dR_1}{dB} + R_2\frac{dR_2}{dB}\right) + aR_3\frac{dR_3}{dB} = 0 \qquad \text{(VIII.25)}$$

where:

$$\int_0^{3l} M\frac{dM}{dB}\,dx = B\int_0^{3l} x^6\,dx = \frac{(3l)^7}{7}B;$$

$$R_1\frac{dR_1}{dB} = 36Bl^4$$

* Other assumptions including $R = B\sin\frac{\pi}{6l}x$ have been investigated. That choice gives a solution identical to the strain-energy solution of para. 4 above. The choice of $M = Bx^2$ seems inappropriate because it is found then that $R_1 = R_2 = R_4 = R_5$. The choice of $R = B_1 + B_2\sin\frac{\pi}{6l}x$ has not been explored.

$$R_2 \frac{dR_2}{dB} = 144Bl^4$$

$$R_3 \frac{dR_3}{dB} = -(F-38Bl^2)38l^2$$

Therefore:

$$\frac{EI}{l^3}\frac{dC}{dB} = \frac{2(3l)^7}{7l^3} B+72Bkl^4+288Bkl^4+38^2Bkl^4-38l^2kF = 0 \quad \text{(VIII.26)}$$

If $k = 5$,
$$B = \frac{190}{9645}\frac{F}{l^2}$$

therefore:
$$R_1 = 0{\cdot}118F$$
$$R_2 = 0{\cdot}236F$$
$$R_3 = 0{\cdot}251F$$
$$(R_0 = 0{\cdot}020F)$$

and

$$\Delta_1 = aR_1 = 0{\cdot}590l^3/EI; \quad \Delta_2 = aR_2 = 1{\cdot}180l^3/EI; \quad \Delta_3 = 1{\cdot}255l^3/EI.$$

Also:
$$M_{\text{max}} = 0{\cdot}532lF$$

It is noteworthy that use of a function to represent bending moment M approximately affords much greater simplicity of calculation for this kind of problem than the alternative of using a function to represent distribution of reactive forces R.

6. Summary of solutions

Solutions when $a = 5l^3/EI$

	Strain energy assuming $\Delta = A \sin \frac{\pi}{6l} x$	Exact solution	Complementary energy assuming $M = Bx^3$
R_1	$0{\cdot}121F$	$0{\cdot}113F$	$0{\cdot}118F$
R_2	$0{\cdot}210F$	$0{\cdot}210F$	$0{\cdot}236F$
R_3	$0{\cdot}242F$	$0{\cdot}248F$	$0{\cdot}251F$
M_{max}	$0{\cdot}596lF$	$0{\cdot}595lF$	$0{\cdot}532lF$

NOTE: Δ is deflection; M is bending moment; R_1, R_2, R_3 directly proportional to deflections of elastic supports.

7. Conclusions.

(*a*) The potential-energy method is perhaps the easiest to apply reliably in general, because of the frequent readiness with which deflection patterns can be envisaged. Thus, in the problem considered, the choice of the simple form $\Delta = A \sin \frac{\pi}{6l} x$ as satisfying the geometrical boundary conditions could be described as being obvious. Due to the usual nature of deflection curves whereby discontinuities are absent, trigonometrical series are well suited for dealing with more complicated problems. Some simplification is always possible if symmetrical and anti-symmetrical components of a problem can be detected.

(*b*) The complementary-energy method suffers from the disadvantage that it is not usually easy to visualize (without preliminary calculations) the nature of bending moment or force distributions especially with regard to discontinuities. For the problem considered obvious possibilities are: $R = B \sin \frac{\pi}{6l} x$ and $M = D \sin \frac{\pi}{6l} x$ as desirably simple forms which can satisfy the boundary conditions of equilibrium. The former is, however, merely another way of specifying that $\Delta = A \sin \frac{\pi}{6l} x$ and is, therefore, incapable of providing an alternative solution to that of the potential or strain energy method. The latter represents a bad choice of bending moment distribution because there is, in fact, a discontinuity of bending moment at C. A more appropriate choice (with maximum simplicity) is $M = Bx^3$ for one-half of the span, i.e. between $x = 0$ and $3l$. (Since the bending moment is discontinuous any continuous function can only specify values at discrete points such as the supports in this instance.)

(*c*) The results shown in the table indicate that the potential-energy method gives an underestimate or lower bound of maximum deflection at a load while the complementary-energy method gives an underestimate or lower bound of maximum bending moment, provided that bending moment has been represented approximately. These features are consistent with the implication of extra stiffness when deflection is approximated and, on the other hand, reduction of stiffness due to some violation of strain compatibility when bending moment is represented approximately. If the two alternative energy solutions are truly independent in the sense that the approximating functions chosen are not merely different ways of specifying one physical quantity (as when the same function is used to represent deflection and elastic support reactions in the present problem), it will usually happen that the maximum bending moment obtained from the potential-energy solution and the maximum deflection from the complementary-energy solution represent upper bounds for those quantities respectively. (It will be noted that in the table, the maximum bending moments by the exact- and potential-energy solutions are almost identical, so discouraging any tendency to assume that exact solutions are necessarily nearly midway between those of the two energy methods.) It is interesting to observe that if the two energy solutions are not independent, as when $\Delta = A \sin \frac{\pi}{6l} x$ and $R = B \sin \frac{\pi}{6l} x$ (for the elastic supports only) in the present problem, the final results are identical. Thus the maximum deflection is underestimated and the maximum bending moment overestimated by both solutions. Moreover, the maximum force obtained directly from the complementary-energy solution is underestimated (being consistent with underestimate of deflection by the potential energy method) and to that somewhat trivial extent that solution is in accordance with expectation. That feature does, however, call attention to the fact that whereas the potential-energy method provides, secondarily, an overestimate of the maximum bending moment it necessarily provides an underestimate of the maximum elastic support reaction in the kind of problem considered.

Appendix I
The Law of Conservation of Energy in Theory of Structures

1. History.

Although the principle of virtual work was identified as long ago as the thirteenth century (Jordanus Nemorius) it was not related explicitly to the concept of conservation of energy. According to Maxwell the latter concept was implicitly stated by Newton in his treatment of the third law of motion and can be detected in some of Euler's work (1744 after D. Bernoulli), but Riccati* (1754) seems to have priority for its use in relation to elastic strain. Young (1807) was concerned with resilience and fracture of materials, it seems, but it is to Poncelet (1831) that introduction of the conservation of energy concept into applied or practical mechanics is probably due. Moseley (1843) quotes Poncelet's teaching of bending of elastic beams and his equation of work done by a load and the related strain energy of a beam. He also noted that $\frac{dU}{d\Delta} = F$ and attempted to calculate deflection of beams by energy derivatives. (Earlier, in 1833, Moseley had published a paper on what he called " the principle of least resistance " for the analysis of arches and had used what might be described as the theologico-metaphysical approach whereby energy concepts had appeared within the discipline of Natural Philosophy.)

Subsequently Lamé (1852) gave an account of what he called Clapeyron's Theorem for elastic systems in general. Apparently Clapeyron (1833) had used the principle of virtual work to establish that 2 (strain energy) = 2 (work done by impressed forces) for linearly elastic bodies, without even mentioning conservation of energy as such! Indeed it was to Clapeyron's theorem that J. Clerk Maxwell referred in 1864 in the course of his celebrated work on analysis of statically-indeterminate frameworks, though he did mention the implication that energy is conserved.

Cotterill in 1865 finally provided an important clue to the general possibilities of the conservation of energy concept in theory of statically-indeterminate systems, but his work remained largely unnoticed until quite recently. This Appendix is concerned with suggesting useful derivations which are based upon the concept of conservation of energy alone.

2. Law of conservation applied generally to elastic structures.

Regardless of the law of elasticity:

Strain energy (U) = work done by loading (W) for any specified loading, where U is the increase in strain energy associated with that loading only.

* A pupil of Euler.

If the structure has n degrees of freedom of deflection specified by the n independent geometrically compatible quantities $\Delta_1, \Delta_2, \ldots, \Delta_n$ then:

$$\frac{\partial U}{\partial \Delta_i} = \frac{\partial W}{\partial \Delta_i} \quad (i = 1, 2, \ldots, n)$$

and thereby n independent equations of equilibrium in the unknowns Δ and known loads F may be derived. Alternatively, it may be said that for a state of equilibrium the function $\phi = (U - W)$ is stationary in respect of variation of deflection or displacement. This can be used for deriving the final equations of the equilibrium or displacement approach for the analysis of a structure. But it is, perhaps, more useful for the purpose of obtaining approximate solutions for complex structures (e.g. grids and suspension bridges), whose deflection pattern may be expressed approximately by a series of functions which satisfy the geometrical boundary conditions (see Chap. VIII).

On a more elementary level the deflection at the point of application and in the line of action, of a single load of an elastic structure may be found simply by using the equation:

$$U = \int_0^e T\,de = U = \int_0^\Delta F\,d\Delta$$

where T and e are the force and extension of a member if a truss is envisaged. This procedure may be generalized, however, by using the *concept of the virtual structure* (see para. 3).

Again, envisaging a truss whose elasticity is linear throughout, by virtue of linear elasticity of its members and " constant geometry ":

$$U = \tfrac{1}{2}\sum Te = W = \tfrac{1}{2}\sum F\Delta$$

or

$$2U = \sum Te = 2W = \sum F\Delta$$

Now the relationship $\sum Te = \sum F\Delta$ merits careful attention. That relationship can be held to be valid for *any* structure with *any* law of elasticity provided that the constant geometry condition is fulfilled.* Thus the relationship between T and e and F and Δ may follow any path, linear or non-linear, or in other words, for a set of forces T and F in equilibrium and a set of compatible displacements e and Δ associated with that set of forces:

$$\sum Te = \sum F\Delta$$

regardless of the path whereby the e's and Δ's are attained. But in general:

$$2U \neq 2W \neq \sum Te = \sum F\Delta$$

In fact Cottcrill (1865) interested himself in the relationship for linearly elastic systems, namely:

$$2U = \sum Te = \sum F\Delta$$

and derived:

$$2\delta U = \sum T\,\delta e + \sum e\,\delta T = \sum F\,\delta\Delta + \sum \Delta\,\delta F$$

Then noting that

$$\delta U = \sum T\,\delta e = \sum F\,\delta\Delta$$

by definition of U, he concluded that alternatively,

$$\delta U = \sum e\,\delta T = \sum \Delta\,\delta F$$

and proceeded to derive therefrom:

$$\frac{\partial U}{\partial F} = \Delta$$

* For imagine a structure with members whose elasticity is the same and such that $U = k\,\Sigma\,Te$ (where k is a constant); then the work done by the loading in small displacements compatible with constant geometry will be such that $W = k\,\Sigma\,F\Delta$ whence, since $U = W$, $\Sigma\,Te = \Sigma\,F\Delta$.

for linear systems some eight years before Castigliano's work. Had he considered the matter further he might well have noted the inherent generality of his approach and that $\sum e\,\delta T = \sum \Delta\,\delta F = \delta C$, the variation of complementary energy which, by the foregoing, is valid for non-linear elasticity (with constant geometry) and affords the general form of derivative for deflection:

$$\frac{\partial C}{\partial F} = \Delta$$

a feature which was left to Engesser to expound in 1889.

3. Principle of virtual structures and conservation of energy for calculating deflection.

The deflections (small) of any structure caused by any specified loading can be reproduced in another structure of geometrically identical shape by some other specified loading if appropriate elastic properties are specified for the members of elements of the geometrically identical (virtual) structure. This might be termed the *Principle of virtual structures*.

It can be used to enable the deflection of any point of a specified structure due to any specified loading to be calculated simply by using the concept of conservation of energy applied to the virtual structure with a single arbitrary load acting in the appropriate direction at the point whose deflection is required. Moreover, since the deformations of the elements of the virtual structure caused by the single load are specified as being identical to those of the corresponding elements of the actual structure due to the loading of that structure, the nature of the elasticity of the virtual structure may be assumed to be linear in all cases for the sake of convenience (i.e. even if the elasticity of the actual structure is non-linear). For example, referring to the problem of Chapter IV, § 14; there the loaded structure shown in fig. IV.13 is analysed and the vertical deflection of the joint Q is obtained using the virtual work concept. By the concept of virtual structures, however, the governing equations of deflection (IV.48 and IV.53) are obtained by conservation of energy. Thus for the former, the structure shown in fig. IV.15 is regarded as a virtual or imaginary structure whose elastic properties are such that the applied forces T'_{EG} shown cause precisely the same small changes in length of the various members as are caused in the actual structure (fig. IV.14) due to the prescribed loading F_{PV} and T_{EG}. Then application of the law of conservation of energy to the virtual (linear) structure gives equation (IV.48) once the constant factor of one half is cancelled on both sides of the energy equation. Again, equation (IV.53) may be derived by conservation of energy regarding the structure shown in fig. IV.16 as a structure wherein the small elastic changes in length of the members caused by the load F''_{PV} are identical to those caused by forces T_{EG} applied to the actual structure *BEDCQB* at E and B, as shown in fig. IV.14.

REFERENCES

1. Maxwell, J. Clerk, *Matter and Motion*. SPCK, London, 1877.
2. Todhunter, I., and Pearson, K., *A history of the theory of elasticity and strength of materials*, vol. i. Cambridge University Press, 1866.
3. Moseley, H., *The mechanical principles of engineering and architecture*. Longmans, 1843.
4. Lamé, G., *Leçons sur la théorie mathématique de l'élasticité des corps solides*. Gauthier-Villars, Paris, 1852.
5. Cotterill, J. H., " On the equilibrium of arched ribs of uniform section ", *Phil. Mag.*, 4th ser., **29**, 380, 430, 1865.

Appendix II

Strain Compatibility Conditions of Grossly Distorted Structures by Virtual Work*

The apparent inadequacy of energy methods, for the purpose of deriving conditions of compatibility of strains involving gross distortion of elastic frameworks is demonstrated in Chapter V. The purpose of this appendix is to show that the principle of virtual work can be used to this end. Libove has already shown that the problem of compatibility conditions involving gross distortion can be treated by using a novel quantity which he calls " total complementary energy " on the basis of an analogy to total potential energy.

The virtual work method is easily demonstrated by means of a simple example. The two-bar, pin-jointed elastic system shown in fig. 1 is such that gross distortion is inevitable if there is a load component at P perpendicular to the initial line OPQ of the two bars. Thus, to resist such a load component F, the bars assume a configuration OP′Q defined by their extensions e or the angles ϕ between OP′ and OP and between P′Q and PQ, if the elastic properties of the bars are similar. If now the loaded system is considered to suffer compatible virtual displacements (i.e. virtual displacements which are compatible with the geometry of the loaded system) such that it is magnified to twice its actual size as shown in fig. 1, the corresponding equation of virtual work is:

$$2(l+e)T - 2lT\cos\phi + Fh \qquad (1)$$

where T is the tension in each bar, $T\cos\phi$ is the component of the reaction at O and Q in the line OQ, and h is the deflection PP′ in the line of action of the load F. Therefore:†

$$2(l+e)\,\delta T = 2l\delta(T\cos\phi)+h\,\delta F$$

or

$$2(l+e)\,\delta T = 2l\,\delta T\cos\phi - 2lT\sin\phi\,\delta\phi + h\,\delta F \qquad (2)$$

for small changes in the variables T, F, and ϕ which are subject to the conditions of equilibrium

$$F = 2T\sin\phi$$

$$(T\cos\phi = T\cos\phi) \qquad (3)$$

whence

$$\delta F = 2\delta T\sin\phi + 2T\cos\phi\,\delta\phi$$

or

$$\delta\phi = (\delta F - 2\delta T\sin\phi)/(2T\cos\phi) \qquad (4)$$

Thus, by making use of equations 3 and 4, ϕ may be eliminated from equation 2 to give:

$$2(l+e)\,\delta T = l\,\frac{(4T^2-F^2)^{\frac{1}{2}}\,\delta T}{T} - l\,\frac{F\,\delta F}{(4T^2-F^2)^{\frac{1}{2}}} - l\,\frac{F^2\,\delta T}{T(4T^2-F^2)^{\frac{1}{2}}} + h\,\delta F \qquad (5)$$

* This appendix, written by Professor T. M. Charlton, was originally published as an article in *Civil Engineering and Public Works Review*, March 1963. It is reproduced by kind permission of the publishers of that periodical.

† This step is justified by considering general variation of equation (1), neglecting small quantities of the second order, and noting that $2T\,\delta e = F\,\delta h$ by virtual work.

in which δT and δF are independent in respect of the requirements of equilibrium, so that

$$2(l+e) = l(4T^2-F^2)^{\frac{1}{2}}/T - lF^2/T(4T^2-F^2)^{\frac{1}{2}} \tag{6}$$

and

$$0 = h - lF/(4T^2-F^2)^{\frac{1}{2}} \tag{7}$$

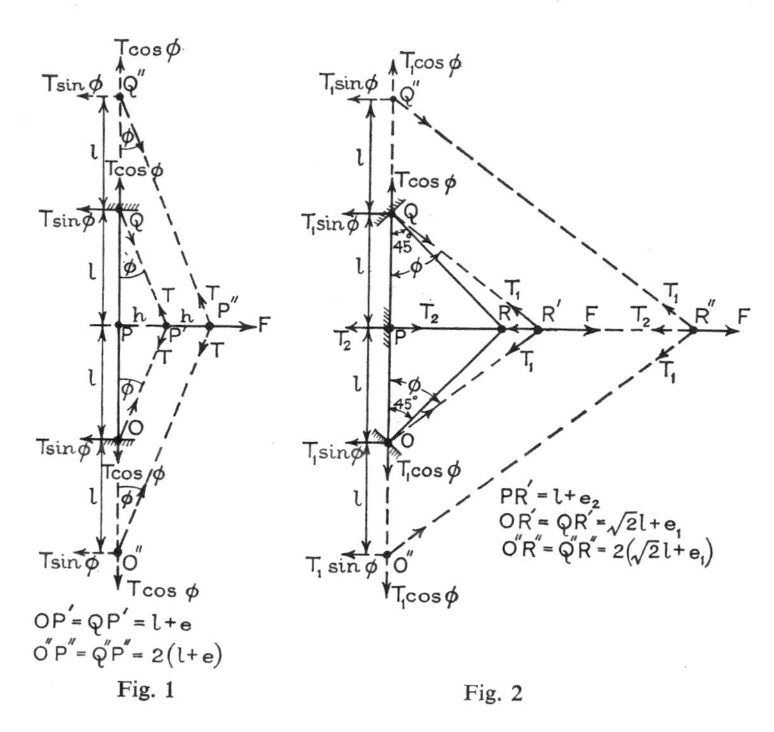

Fig. 1

Fig. 2

Equation 6 is a strain compatibility equation which provides a means of obtaining T in terms of F, provided that the law of elasticity of the bars is specified and e can be expressed as a function of T. Equation 7 merely specifies that

$$h = l \tan \phi \tag{8}$$

These equations can, of course, be derived by direct use of the equations of equilibrium and geometry of the loaded system.

Libove has shown by a different approach that if the " total complementary energy " of the system is defined as

$$C = 2Tl + 2\int e\, dT - 2Tl \cos \phi \tag{9}$$

it can be used to derive an equation connecting F and ϕ once the equilibrium condition of equation 3 is introduced. Equally it can be used to derive equation 6 if ϕ is eliminated by equilibrium instead of T, since it appears that

$$\delta C = 2l\, \delta T + 2e\, \delta T - 2l\, \delta T \cos \phi + 2lT \sin \phi\, \delta\phi = h\, \delta F \tag{10}$$

which is identical to equation 2. Moreover, it seems that the total complementary energy is equal to $\int h\, dF$.

The simple example used above is statically-indeterminate in respect of gross distortion only. For further illustration of the procedure, the framework shown in fig. 2 will be used. This is a plane, pin-jointed elastic framework with one redundant bar, say PR, and gross distortion is assumed to occur due to a load F acting in the line PR. For the sake of simplicity it is assumed that the elastic properties of the bars OR and QR are similar so that the angles between both of them and the line OQ are ϕ after F is applied to the framework. Assuming virtual displacements such that the loaded framework is considered to expand to twice its actual size, the equation of virtual work is

$$2(\surd 2l+e_1)T_1+(l+e_2)T_2 = 2lT_1 \cos\phi+(l+e_2)F \tag{11}$$

where the subscript 1 refers to the bars OR and QR and the subscript 2 refers to the bar PR. Therefore

$$2(\surd 2l+e_1)\,\delta T_1+(l+e_2)\,\delta T_2 = 2l\,\delta(T_1\cos\phi)+(l+e_2)\,\delta F$$

or
$$2(\surd 2l+e_1)\,\delta T_1+(l+e_2)\,\delta T_2 = 2l\,\delta T_1\cos\phi-2lT_1\sin\phi\,\delta\phi+(l+e_2)\,\delta F \tag{12}$$

for small changes in the variables T_1, T_2, F, and ϕ which are subject to the equilibrium condition

$$F = 2T_1\sin\phi+T_2 \tag{13}$$

i.e.
$$\delta F = 2T_1\cos\phi\,\delta\phi+2\delta T_1\sin\phi+\delta T_2$$

whence
$$\delta\phi = (\delta F-2\delta T_1\sin\phi-\delta T_2)/(2T_1\cos\phi) \tag{14}$$

Also, since by equation 13

$$\sin\phi = (F-T_2)/(2T_1)$$
$$\cos\phi = [4T_1^2-(F-T_2)^2]^{\frac{1}{2}}/(2T_1) \tag{15}$$

equation 12 may be rewritten

$$2(\surd 2l+e_1)\,\delta T_1+(l+e_2)\,\delta T_2 = l\,\frac{[4T_1^2-(F-T_2)^2]^{\frac{1}{2}}\,\delta T_1}{T_1}$$
$$-l(F-T_2)\left[\frac{T_1\,\delta F-(F-T_2)\,\delta T_1-T_1\,\delta T_2}{T_1[4T_1^2-(F-T_2)^2]^{\frac{1}{2}}}\right]+(l+e_2)\,\delta F \tag{16}$$

By equating coefficients of the independent quantities δT_1, δT_2, and δF, in turn, the following equations of compatibility of strains are derived

$$2(\surd 2l+e_1) = l[4T_1^2-(F-T_2)^2]^{\frac{1}{2}}/T_1+l(F-T_2)^2/T_1[4T_1^2-(F-T_2)^2]^{\frac{1}{2}} \quad \text{(i)}$$
$$l+e_2 = l(F-T_2)/[4T_1^2-(F-T_2)^2]^{\frac{1}{2}} \quad \text{(ii)} \quad (17)$$
$$0 = -l(F-T_2)/[4T_1^2-(F-T_2)^2]^{\frac{1}{2}}+(l+e_2) \quad \text{(iii)}$$

The second and third of these simultaneous equations are identical, as would be expected, specifying as they do the same condition, namely $l+e_2 = l\tan\phi$. Equations 17 (i) and 17 (ii) are sufficient to enable the values of T_1 and T_2 to be obtained in terms of F provided that the laws of elasticity of the members are specified. Again, if the total complementary energy is

$$C = 2\int(\surd 2l+e_1)\,dT_1+\int(l+e_2)\,dT_2-2l\int d(T_1\cos\phi)\;\left(=\int(l+e_2)\,dF\right) \tag{18}$$

equations 17 represent $\partial C/\partial T_1$, $\partial C/\partial T_2$, and $\partial C/\partial F$ respectively.

It is interesting to compare the above procedure with that which is used ordinarily when there is no gross distortion. Thus, if the framework of fig. 2 is such that the load F does not change its shape and the angles at O and Q after loading are still 45 deg. for practical purposes, then by the principle of virtual work

$$2e_1T_1+e_2T_2 = e_2F \tag{19}$$

and $$2e_1\,\delta T_1+e_2\,\delta T_2 = e_2\,\delta F \tag{20}$$

where C is now the strain complementary energy, and the small changes in the variables T_1, T_2, and F are subject to the condition of equilibrium

$$F = \sqrt{2}T_1+T_2 \quad \text{or} \quad \delta F = \sqrt{2}\delta T_1+\delta T_2 \tag{21}$$

so that $$2e_1\,\delta T_1+e_2\,(\delta F-\sqrt{2}\,\delta T_1) = e_2\,\delta F \tag{22}$$

Hence $$2e_1-\sqrt{2}e_2 = 0 = \partial C/\partial T_1$$

$$e_2 = e_2 = \partial C/\partial F \tag{23}$$

from which T_1 can be found in terms of F when the laws of elasticity of the bars are specified.

There is, however, no reason why the virtual work equation 19 should not be replaced by the form

$$2(\sqrt{2}l+e_1)T_1+(l+e_2)T_2-2lT_1\cos 45 = (l+e_2)F \tag{24}$$

by using compatible virtual displacements which would imply the loaded system magnification to twice its actual size. Thus

$$2(\sqrt{2}l+e_1)\,\delta T_1+(l+e_2)\,\delta T_2-\sqrt{2}l\,\delta T_1 = (l+e_2)\,\delta F(= \delta C) \tag{25}$$

where C is the *total* complementary energy. Whence

$$2(\sqrt{2}l+e_1)-\sqrt{2}(l+e_2)-\sqrt{2}l = 0 = \partial C/\partial T_1$$

or $$2e_1-\sqrt{2}e_2 = 0$$

$$l+e_2 = l+e_2 = \partial C/\partial F \tag{26}$$

or $$e_2 = e_2$$

It appears, then, that the general virtual work procedure requires the use of virtual magnification (or contraction) of the loaded structure as a whole. By this means both small and large strains and deflections can be considered and it is possible to identify a total complementary energy quantity which, as Libove suggests, can be used for obtaining approximate solutions to complex problems involving large strains.

REFERENCE

LIBOVE, C. *Principle of stationary complementary energy for structures with finite deformations.* Syracuse University Research Institute Report, ME 836–624, New York, 1962.

Bibliography

1. MAXWELL, J. C., " On the calculation of the equilibrium and stiffness of frames ", *Phil. Mag.*, 4th ser., **27,** 294, 1864.
2. JENKIN, FLEEMING, " Braced arches and suspension bridges ", *Proc. R. Scot. Soc. Arts*, **8,** 135, 1869. (Virtual velocities.)
3. BETTI, E., *Il nuovo cimento*, ser. 2, **7** and **8,** Milan, 1872.
4. RAYLEIGH, BARON, " A statical theorem ", *Phil. Mag.*, 4th ser., **48,** 452, 1874 and **49,** 183, 1875.
5. CASTIGLIANO, A., " Nuova teoria intorno all'equilibrio dei sistemi elastici ", *Trans. Acad. Sc. Turin*, **10,** 380, 1875. (Based on a thesis to the University of Turin, 1873.)
6. CASTIGLIANO, A., *Elastic stresses in structures.* Scott, Greenwood, London, 1919. (Translation from the Italian edition of 1879 by E. S. Andrews.)
7. SWAIN, G. F., " On the application of the principle of virtual velocities to the determination of the deflections and stresses of frames ", *J. Franklin Inst.*, **183,** 102, 1883.
8. CROTTI, F., *La teoria dell'elasticita.* Heopli, Milan, 1888.
9. ENGESSER, F., " Über statisch unbestimmte Träger bei beliebigem Formänderungsgesetze und über den Satz von der kleinsten Ergänzungsarbeit ", *Z. d. Arch. u. Ing. Ver. z. Hannover*, **35,** col. 733, 1889.
10. LAMB, E. H., " The principle of virtual velocities and its application to the theory of elastic structures ", *I.C.E. Select. Engg. Paper*, **10,** 1923.
11. SOUTHWELL, R. V., " On Castigliano's theorem of least work and the principle of St. Venant ", *Phil. Mag.*, 7th ser., **45,** 193, 1923.
12. TEMPLE, G., and BICKLEY, W. G., *Rayleigh's principle and its applications to engineering.* Oxford University Press, 1933.
13. WILLIAMS, D., " Relations between the energy theorems applicable in structural theory ", *Phil. Mag.*, 7th ser., **60,** 617, 1938.
14. WESTERGAARD, H. M., " On the method of complementary energy ", *Proc. A.S.C.E.*, **67,** 199, 1941.
15. VAN DEN BROEK, J. A., *Elastic energy theory*, 2nd ed. John Wiley, New York, 1942. (1st ed. 1933.)
16. CHARLTON, T. M., " Some notes on the analysis of redundant systems by means of the conception of conservation of energy ", *J. Franklin Inst.*, **250,** 543, 1950.
17. PARLAND, H., *Om elasticitetsteorins variationsprinciper.* Helsinki, 1951.
18. CHARLTON, T. M., " Analysis of statically-indeterminate structures by the complementary energy method ", *Engineering*, **174,** 389, 1952.
19. LANGHAAR, H. L., " The principle of complementary energy in non-linear elasticity theory ", *J. Franklin Inst.*, **256,** 255, 1953.
20. CHARLTON, T. M., *Energy principles in applied statics.* Blackie, London, 1959.
21. MATHESON, J. A. L., *Hyperstatic structures*, vol. 1. Butterworths, London, 1959.
22. YLINEN, A., and ESKOLA, A., " Theory of a statically-indeterminate pin-jointed framework the material of which does not follow Hooke's law ", *Proc. International Association for Bridge and Structural Engineering*, **6,** 167, 1960.
23. LANGHAAR, H. L., *Energy methods in applied mechanics.* John Wiley, New York, 1962.
24. NEAL, B. G., *Structural theorems and their applications.* Pergamon, Oxford, 1964.

25. BOWEN, C. F., and CHARLTON, T. M., " A note on the approximate analysis of suspension bridges ", *The Structural Engineer*, **45**, 241, 1967.
26. GREGORY, M. S., *Introduction to extremum principles*. Butterworths, London, 1969.
27. CHARLTON, T. M., *Principles of structural analysis*. Longmans, London, 1969.
28. CHARLTON, T. M., " Maxwell, Jenkin and Cotterill and the theory of statically-indeterminate structures ", *R.S., Notes and Records*, **26**, 233, 1971.
29. COATES, R. C., COUTIE, M. G., and KONG, F. K., *Structural Analysis*. Nelson, London, 1972.

Index